To Wendy

C000241

RUNNING ON THE
SPECTRUM

Hope you enjoy my
story as fellow
runners and spotarossons

Regards Gene

GENE MORAN

Denbigh November
2022

© Gene Chris Moran 2022
Illustrations © Gene Chris Moran 2022
Cover image from Pixabay

Published by
Jelly Bean Books, Mackintosh House
136 Newport Road, Cardiff, CF24 1DJ
www.candyjarbooks.co.uk
ISBN: 978-1-915439-20-8

Editor: Keren Williams
Editorial: Ben Jones

Printed and bound in the UK by
Severn, Bristol Road, Gloucester, GL2 5EU

To:

those who made me think
those who made me laugh
and those who made me cry

thank you, as without you this book would
never have been written.

PS. If you think one of my characters is
based on you – they probably are!

Although *Running on the Spectrum* is
autobiographical in nature and inspired
by true events, many of the locations,
names and dates have been changed for
dramatic purposes. Some of the
characters may also be amalgamations
or completely fictitious, and any
similarity to actual persons is entirely
coincidental.

Denise Deegan:

"I loved reading this engrossing tale, which draws you in from the start. Its unique rhythm and different strands including running and training are explained methodically so that they can be followed by anyone. This story gives a first person account of autism which works very well throughout the story. Full of humour and never dull it is also very moving at times."

Denise is an English novelist best known for her play 'Daisy pulls it off'. She is based in North Wales where, as well as continuing her career as a writer, she has also found time to be a member of her local Mountain Rescue Team. (More information is available on Wikipedia.)

Bill Gribble:

"A heart-warming read that shows, given the right encouragement and guidance, even the most troubled and lost young people can achieve their true potential. Society does get the children and young people it deserves. If we fail to invest appropriately at an early stage, we create casualties to society's cost."

Bill was a headteacher as well as a consultant and advisor in Social, Emotional and Behavioural Disorders. He is the author of 'In a class of your own – Managing pupils' behaviour'.

Geoff Edwards:

"It is a pleasure to accompany Tom the protagonist as he takes us through his emotional journey as an energetic teacher, who through self-preservation and personal interest, tries to develop a culture where pupils can manage their freedom in society. The 'true to life' incidents within the story are absorbing and amusing anecdotes surrounding all matters both in and out of the classroom.

His tales with insightful observations and personal walking and running experiences across North Wales may well have been told before, but not with such freshness and realism. Larger-than-life characters are discovered and endearing and disarming qualities of the school children acknowledged. Through Tom's time at Ysgol Abaty we come to know Eve, one of the students and the thread of the life journey she takes with Tom is a vital part of the story. It is told with an unapologetically realistic delivery and with emotions from all sides, which provides us with a realistic view of the school community. The ending is both a fitting and inevitable one and simply put 'A joy and must to read'."

Geoff was an OFSTED school inspector for over twenty years and a CDT trained specialist teacher.

Patricia Sumner:

"*Running on the Spectrum* is an engaging, touching and often humorous story about Tom Mallalieu who teaches at a North Wales school for pupils with special educational needs and emotional/behavioural difficulties. The story describes the relationships Tom develops with both staff and students, and the running club he establishes at the school which gives the students a sense of purpose, hope and pride. The beautiful scenery of Snowdonia and the Clwydian Hills form the backdrop to the story, and a real sense of the culture of North Wales is achieved. Though some aspects of the story are very moving, the author never strays into sentimentality. The story is told in a frank, uncomplicated and often amusing way, which is highly engaging. The author's enthusiasm for running, for the great outdoors, for Snowdonia, for teaching and for people in general shines through in this novel. I loved it; it's an insightful and heart-warming read."

Pat, a former teacher, is a writer and editor living in North Wales. She has written and had published several children's books, a collection of poetry and the educational resources 'Creativity Through Language Book 1: How to teach fictional writing' *and* 'Creativity Through Language Book 2: How to teach informative/non-fictional writing' *(published by Lawler Education).*

Finlay Wild:

"It was great to be taken back to the mountains of Snowdonia by this enjoyable read. Following some of the characters on their journey to the Welsh 3000s and beyond was an illuminating reminder of the value of exercise and mountains for all."

Finlay is a Scottish runner and skier and is known amongst the hill-running community as a record breaker. He is the current holder of the Welsh 3000s' record (in 4 hrs, 10 mins, 48 secs), breaking Colin Donnelly's record held since 1988, and he has been the winner of the Ben Nevis Race every year so far since 2010, giving him ten wins more than anyone else in the history of the event. (More information is available on Wikipedia.)

Gareth Williams OBE:
"An interesting, often humorous account of life in a special school set in North Wales, from the first day in Tom's new job to having to say goodbye to students, friends and colleagues at the end of his time there. Each chapter clearly describes the excitement, the fear and nervousness of working with children on the Spectrum. Three main themes stand out throughout the book: Trust, Relationships and Success. North Wales and Snowdonia in particular as its setting help strengthen the story. When you put all these factors together, you can expect the unexpected!"

Gareth was born in North Wales and speaks Welsh as his first language. After an initial period on the professional footballer stage, he went on to teach in various sectors of education including Pupil Referral Units. He ended his educational career as a National Leader in Education and a principal of a residential Special School in England, which under his leadership gained several outstanding OFSTED reports.

Keren Williams:
"A very interesting and well-rounded book with a very uplifting and heart-warming story. It's a thoroughly enjoyable read from start to finish."

Having gained a Masters of Arts in English Literature and Creative Writing at Cardiff Metropolitan University, Keren is currently publishing co-ordinator at Candy Jar Books.

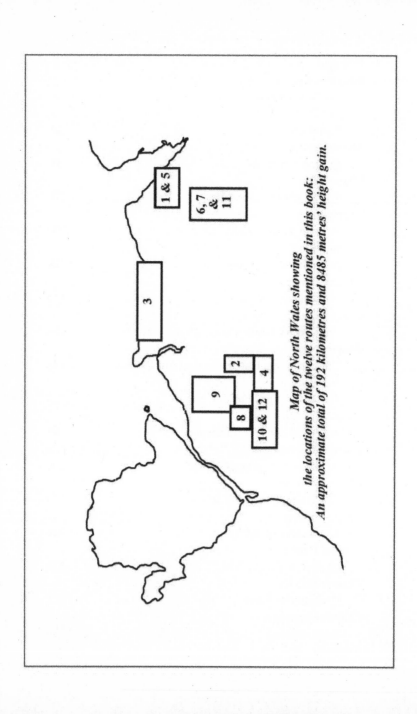

Map of North Wales showing
the locations of the twelve routes mentioned in this book:
An approximate total of 192 kilometres and 8485 metres' height gain.

Prologue

Song lyrics were echoing around the deserted school
grounds. The wide range of notes, from high to low,
seemed to drift across the air in no particular direction.
The notes disturbed the metronomic rhythm of the rain
on the car roof. Like the rain, the source of the singing
came from high above the car.

Leaning across the passenger seat for a better view, I
could just see the row of old wooden sash windows on
the third floor of the rundown building. One window had
been pushed open to its fullest. The curtains were blowing
wildly in the wind. A child – of about eleven years old, I
thought – was clambering out of the window, paying no
regard at all to the danger involved. This was the source
of the boy soprano voice, competing with the pounding
rain.

Memories of June 1968 immediately came flooding
back, though at that time the lyrics of that particular song
were sung in the famous baritone voice of the decade. I

smiled, recalling my sister playing her new 7" vinyl single at full volume in her bedroom, much to the annoyance of my father – though my mother didn't seem to mind as much! It's still a wonder to me why Delilah wasn't a more popular girl's name then, due to the popularity of 'Tom the Voice', as my mother always dubbed Tom Jones[1].

Glancing up again at the old building, the child, within a matter of seconds, had used a two-handed push-up to get over the cast-iron guttering and was onto the slippery, slated roof above. With his shoulder-length blond hair, and dressed in a white tracksuit top and bottoms, he reminded me of a negative film image from a 1950s Box Brownie camera. Perhaps he was a ninja escaping a crime scene, after a deadly deed had been committed in the gloomy morning rain? Then, like a figment of my imagination, he was gone.

Chapter One
My New Environment

All educational professionals and school children know that as soon as the summer holidays finish, the sun usually comes out and the rain stops. But not this time! This time the weather seemed to be changing for the worse. An omen of things to come, perhaps?

It was Tuesday, 1st September 2015 and my first day at work after the summer holidays. Just as on my interview day, when I'd arrived ten minutes early, I'd made a point of being one of the first to arrive at Ysgol Abaty. From my experience at other schools, I knew that 7:30am would be far earlier than most staff members would arrive on the scene, so I'd planned my arrival time for 7:20am. This would give me my required ten minutes of contemplation time before I exited my car and made my way over to the school. But, as the traffic was surprisingly light that morning, I'd decided to pull over in a lay-by on Well Hill to maintain my strict schedule.

As well as being precise about arrival times, parking

in the same spot in car parks is a desire – maybe even a need – of mine, and has been throughout my driving, or should I say 'parking', life. I've always found it necessary to have control and consistency around me, and my parking habits are just one aspect of this. My family and friends who know me well always find my parking antics amusing, especially when my desired space isn't available and I have to make at least two tours of the car park before any decision can be made. Although, when questioned, friends and family have never been able to deny that they usually seek out the same area of the local supermarket to park up themselves when getting their weekly shop. It isn't as important to them as it is to me but, in reality, it's a small characteristic of autism that many of us share.

As I put on the handbrake, the dashboard clock reads 07:19am. Not perfect, but within the time limit of plus or minus two minutes that I'd set myself. My Skoda was a typical teacher's car – cheap and easy to repair. It was one of only three cars parked in the morning downpour. The day before, I'd washed and polished its white paintwork so that it would be clean and shiny for my first day at my new job. But the spray from the other vehicles en route to work, and the mud collected from the car park, had made this a pointless chore. Now, the endless streaks of grime and mud would allow it to blend in easily with the gamekeepers' vehicles at any safari park.

I wondered who owned the other two cars located at opposite ends of the rough gravel parking area. One was an old Volkswagen Beetle, which must once have been bright orange in colour. Now it was a mixture of orange and grey, resulting in an impressive camouflage effect – though where that would be useful, I wasn't sure. The 'K' at the start of the registration plate made it circa 1972 (the same year I'd left school), and so, in retrospect, for a forty-plus-year-old car, it looked quite good.

I found it amusing that I'd grown up within ten minutes' walk of this school, yet had never noticed the building, let alone known that the school existed. The school was located on the lower rolling hills of the Greenfield Valley near Holywell. I'd ventured down the concealed driveway for the first time only five months ago on Wednesday the 1st of April. There had only been two differences that had stood out to me that day. The first was the information that there was no uniform for the pupils to wear and that members of staff also wore casual clothes. The second was the knowledge that members of staff were known by their first names. So, after years of being referred to as Mr Mallalieu, I was now going to be called Tom.

One of the governors, while firmly shaking my hand after the interview, had explained to me, 'This isn't a school where you gain respect because of a name or a title. Here, respect is earned because of who you are and not what you're called.'

One added bonus was that students would no longer keep asking me, with mischief in their voices, 'Are you from France, sir?'

Whether I'd been a fool accepting this job, I'd soon find out.

The scene in front of me bore little resemblance to the one I'd witnessed on the glorious spring morning of my interview, it had been peaceful, even tranquil and, probably most importantly of all, there were no students around. The negative ninja running along the high rooftops at 7:20am had made me realise that the tranquillity of my interview day would soon be a memory. Now that I could see no trace of him, I wondered if he'd been real or imaginary – or even one of the many recollections I constantly seem to conjure up. After all, why else would he have been there so early in the morning?

The long driveway to Ysgol Abaty (which translates from Welsh as 'Abbey School') was a patchwork of potholes. Some had made makeshift repairs; others had been left as traps for drivers or walkers, unaware of their depth when they were filled with rainwater. As I sat surveying the environment around me, the fetid wet leaves triggered memories from my younger days of running past the school entrance as the winter nights drew in. Then I'd always been concentrating on my pace or time as I passed by, not on the type of establishment that might lie beyond the gates.

Ysgol Abaty was on one of my favourite running routes from my youth. I'd spent endless hours in my old Ford Escort driving along the roads and lanes circling the Holywell/Greenfield Valley. Having set my trip meter to zero, I'd then, with great care and accuracy, note buildings, trees and hedges as controls to remind me where the different mile points were. These would then act as my pace setters as I carried out my training runs. However, now, each new spring, when I take in the fragrance of freshly cut hedges, I'm reminded that mischief can be about. How I cursed at the end of one run when I discovered that a local farmer had cut his hedge without telling me! By doing so, he'd repositioned one of my carefully selected controls. I knew that my repetitive miles on this course were always within five seconds of each other. With my time for the six-mile run being pleasingly, and surprisingly, over two minutes quicker, it was only when I drove the course again that I realised the hedge had been cut back. I concluded that in future I'd need a backup control, just in case the hedges were trimmed. This, of course, was long before the days of personal GPS systems or the many apps that are available today. The current range of sporting apps was only being dreamt of in my early days of running.

Often, I was able to extend my runs by simply putting different shorter routes together. This would result in demanding length and height gains, with hills that would test most mountain marathoners, perhaps even Joss Naylor[2]. Well, once he'd got into his eighties at least!

The misted screen of my 2008 Fabia was now becoming impossible to see through as I sat in the near-vacant car park, collecting my thoughts and steadying my nerves. I leant over to the passenger side and used my beanie hat, which had fallen out of my rucksack after my last walk on the hills, to clear the side window of the increasing condensation. Through the partially cleared window, I could see back to the two ornamental gates that guarded the school entrance. Once they'd have suggested the grand splendour of the great Victorian house that lay behind them. Now, they were forced wide open, brown with rust and showing little evidence of the brilliant white paint that I recalled from my training-run days. The building was completely screened off from the road by a high wall and rows of tall poplar trees. Also spaced around the grounds were two wonderful mature oaks and several horse-chestnut trees, further evidence of its rich past. It looked like a fire escape had been added to the building, and in doing so it had obscured the original main entrance. A brick and glass surround had been added in front of the fire escape, which provided some protection from the elements. The elevation was ugly in every sense of the word. It must have been funded, or part-funded, by the local council. Otherwise, it would never have been granted planning permission!

I checked the time again and found it to be 7:30am. I'd taken my required ten minutes to gather my thoughts. I didn't have a chance to register the second vehicle as the time, as well as the lighter rain on the car roof, was my cue to sprint for the newly extended entrance, in the hope of not getting my clothes too wet. It was now or never! I took a deep breath and ran.

As soon as I'd entered the building, the familiar waft of a new school year filled my senses. The mixture of floor polish and the newly painted classrooms was obvious to a well-trained nose like mine. I find I'm constantly taken back to previous times and events by the smells I inhale. I know others are also reminded of past times by evocative odours, but unlike them, I often find I take the time to relive and relish them. This is another one of the many things others don't understand about me. Unlike the line in William Henry Davies' poem, '*We have no time to stand and stare*'[3], I always seem to create the time. In fact, it's a reflex action of mine, which I seem to have little choice about. Flashbacks of decorating and far too many summer holiday makeovers filled my thoughts. It looked like this August makeover would be enough to hide the cracks, old staples and poor design for yet another school year, but not for much longer.

I leant forward and shook myself, in an effort to remove some of the excess rain from my clothes and hair. Unfortunately, during my dash, I hadn't allowed for the frequency and hidden depth of the potholes. My shoes, along with the bottom section of my trouser legs, looked like they'd been used on one of my old cross-country runs. Then, once I'd completed the distance, I'd run a hosepipe over them, a technique learned during my mountain marathon days. If a hosepipe wasn't available then, once over the finishing line, a paddle in a convenient stream to wash off excess mud was always a good idea. Neither of these options was available on this occasion.

As I looked down at the highly polished, oak, herringbone-patterned floor, I swallowed hard. I'd left a trail of water and muddy footprints from the entrance to the narrow receptionist's hatch. This was certainly not the first impression I wanted to make, so without a mountain stream or even a hosepipe in sight, I decided that the sink in the visitor's toilet at the far end of the corridor was my only option. With stealthy movements, I tried to walk the remaining length of the corridor without actually touching the floor.

Once there, I breathed out and relaxed for a moment. I carefully took off my shoes and started to clean off the excess mud. Using my fingers to sweep away the worst of the mud collected between the sole and heel, I realised it wasn't going to be a quick or easy task. And cleaning my shoes only seemed to make my trousers look worse. As no one else was around yet, I decided to do the job correctly. I took off my jacket and carefully placed it over the top of the cubicle door. Then I rolled up my sleeves and removed my trousers. With renewed confidence, I continued my cleaning spree. After a muddy ten minutes – a time period I hadn't allowed myself – my shoes, at least, looked clean. However, their high polish, evident when I left home, had now disappeared. Unfortunately, the sink, tiles and floor had somehow acquired all the mud from my shoes. Even my carefully rolled-up sleeves were now speckled with mud. There was only one thing for it. With my trousers already removed, I decided to take off my shirt, clean the area again, fully clean my shirt and trousers, dress again and make a rapid exit. So, now semi-naked and quite cold, I made a wad out of the paper towels and set about cleaning the floor.

One of the problems with individual visitor's toilets is that they're unisex, of course. In my attempt to access the room speedily, I hadn't given any thought to locking the door. So I suppose, as it was now after 7:40am, it was inevitable that someone else might come in. I was now on all fours, with only two items of clean clothes on – socks and underpants. The surrounding mud was decreasing, but it was taking more time and paper towels than I'd imagined. I swallowed hard, for the second time, as the door opened wide.

I looked upwards from my crouching position, somewhere between downward and upward dog in yoga, and instinctively gave a hearty, 'Good morning!' to Miss Humphries, the new receptionist, as she froze in the doorway.

Susan Humphries had started at the school on the morning of my interview. Subsequently, we'd chatted at length and shared our mutual sense of nervousness.

Remembering who I was, she responded with an equally hearty, but far quicker, '*Bore da*, Mr Mallalieu,' (the Welsh for 'good morning', as the school management encouraged the use of incidental Welsh wherever possible). Then she quickly turned around and retreated back to the safety of her office.

I'm glad to say this was the last time she referred to me as Mr Mallalieu and, thankfully, the last time she's seen me with no trousers on. I collected more paper towels to try to remove the last traces of mud from the grouting between the white tiles of the sink splash-back, as Miss Humphries was now a witness to the shambles I'd created. With the small room and my attire as clean as I could get them, I slipped into my damp clothes and continued to my classroom.

Did I have a special feeling running through my body as I looked around my new classroom? Was it a sense of the unknown? Or excitement? Or even fear? It was certainly a different feeling to other first days at new schools.

Surely, I thought, *I shouldn't be so nervous.*

After all, I'd taught at several schools, from a highly academic independent college with an average A Level pass rate of 4.8, to a private school run by a group of businessmen, catering for boys and girls permanently excluded from the schools in their local authorities due to 'Emotional and Behavioural Difficulties'. I'd also spent a couple of years on the escape route from teaching, by which I mean I was taking on supply work in several special schools and pupil referral units while looking for a career change. However, Ysgol Abaty was 'special' even when compared with the others. Its official specialist category was a broad one: 'Children with Special Educational Needs and Disabilities'. This allowed it, for political as well as financial reasons, to be open to all special-needs students. The only exception to this was when a student wasn't able to achieve an academic standard that could be recorded on the National Curriculum as their level of understanding was too low. However, this wasn't exactly setting the bar sky-high! The academic and age ranges were as wide as they could be for a secondary school, going from Level One of the National Curriculum to A Level, and the students were between eleven and nineteen years of age.

Wordsworth, the name of the class I had as my form

at Ysgol Abaty, was the most able Key Stage 4 girls' class. Though, as in many special schools, the Key Stages were often blurred to allow for the complex make-up of the individual students who attended them. My class register showed I had a mixture of thirteen, fourteen, fifteen, sixteen and seventeen year olds! In addition, I'd also be teaching Design & Technology, Physical Education and English to other classes.

But before I could even think about teaching the students, I knew I had to be able to manage them. This meant I had to be able to communicate with them or, perhaps more importantly, persuade them to communicate with me. There were going to be six children in the class initially, with two joining later. I was also going to have an LSA or Learning Support Assistant with me. However, some of the other classes I was to teach had three LSAs – an adult-to-student ratio of four staff members to eight students! I knew that alarm bells should be ringing, especially in today's financial climate.

Perhaps, with the benefit of hindsight, as preparation for working at Ysgol Abaty, I'd undertaken two supply teaching posts that would help me in particular. I'd worked at a pupil referral unit, appropriately named Loggerheads. This kind of unit is where a local authority places children for a short period of time, so that they can be assessed and appropriate strategies can be put into place to allow them to return to their mainstream schools as reformed characters and never cause future problems. In the case of Loggerheads, the pupils were placed there for twelve weeks. This always brings to mind a modern abbreviation: LOL. As you might have realised, I do mean 'Laugh Out Loud' and not 'Lots Of Love'.

My last permanent post, and perhaps best preparation for Ysgol Abaty, had been at The Ridall Vocational School. This was an independent school, run by businessmen, with accommodation for students with Emotional and Behavioural Difficulties. It was in Scotland, just fifteen miles from Kilder Water in the heart of the Scottish Borders, and when I left, I was able to take many happy memories with me. Rydell High School, which I first came across in 1978 when I saw what was to become one of the most successful musical films ever, *Grease*, should not be confused with The Ridall Vocational School.

To my surprise, the youngsters attending Ridall actually liked the association with the film and its characters. I would have thought that the songs, cheesy storyline and the lack of sex and violence would have been the 'kiss of death' for it. But no, some of them really loved it; sometimes there's just no comprehending the workings of a teenager's mind – especially as some of the secondary students at Ridall seemed simply to be marking time while making the transition from youth custody to jail! As a private school, it sourced its students from throughout Scotland, England and Wales. Many came from notorious areas, such as Maryhill in Glasgow, Moss Side in Manchester, and the East End of London. Even today, I still wonder which of the students I taught there managed to escape the cycle of crime that they were then caught up in.

Looking around the classroom at Ysgol Abaty, while waiting for my first students to arrive, I wondered if there were any similarities between the two schools. Both had a pupil roll of just fewer than fifty. In both cases, each student had enough special educational needs to persuade their local authority to educate and hostel them out of their home county in England and Wales if necessary. An extravagant option, with a cost often in excess of £125,000 per year at the time!

Chapter Two
Socialising

All in all, I felt I was well prepared for my new role at Ysgol Abaty; I'd had a good holiday, taking advantage of the summer break to rest, and I'd avoided educational matters whenever I could. Unusually, ever since I'd seen the post advertised in the local *Daily Post* the previous February, I'd gained little first-hand knowledge of the school. I was sure that any serious problems would have been local knowledge and would have been passed on to me by friends or family still living in the area. However, some of the classes had three teaching assistants when they contained only eight students! This amount being spent on staff had to be for necessity, not charity. I knew from the copy of the prospectus that I'd been given on my interview day that the school actually had a student-staff ratio, including hostel staff members, that almost equalled one to one!

Just like Ridall, Ysgol Abaty had a hostel, which was situated two miles away. Although a short linear distance, this was by no means a quick jog, even for a past mountain marathoner like myself. This two-mile stretch, almost as straight as the crow flies, included one of the steepest roads in North Wales. Most of the locals would make the round trip up the alternative Brynford Hill and through Holywell Golf Course to get from one place to the other, in order to avoid the steepest part: Pen y Ball Hill.

At Ysgol Abaty, I'd be paid by the hour, so I'd start my directed time at 8:45am and finish at 3:45pm. I would even be given an hour for lunch. Also, included in this time would be a morning and afternoon briefing session. As well as my day-time hours, I'd be required to work for five hours every week during term-time in the hostel, aptly named 'Pen-y-Bryn' (which translates as 'Top of the Hill'). Even better, if I worked over and above my set hours, I'd actually be paid overtime. A second advantage was that they operated a four-term year, meaning that you only ever worked a maximum of five weeks before you had at least a week off. Consequently, my holidays (apart from Easter, Christmas and a few weeks in the summer) were not in line with local authority ones, so great savings could be made.

In order to supplement the hostel staffing rota, my evening duties would be from 4:00pm to 9:00pm on each Tuesday during term-time. So, on my first day of teaching at Ysgol Abaty, I'd be working for over twelve hours! No wonder I was feeling nervous.

As I waited for my first class *Newton* to arrive, my gaze was drawn to a hole in the plasterboard to the right of the classroom door; it was at shoulder height and about the same size as a football. As I pondered its history, the door burst open with a clatter and in they traipsed – five Key Stage 3 girls and one adult – and within a moment, the girls were everywhere.

The introduction by the adult was short.

'I'm Mirain. I was told to tell you I've not worked here before. Also, there's no other staff available for *Newton* today as *Wordsworth* needs them.'

This did little to calm my nerves.

Fortunately, the electric to the power machines in the Design and Technology Room was isolated as one of the girls, her long black ponytail swinging out of the back of her baseball cap, went from one machine to another pushing the 'on' buttons frantically. Another girl, thankfully less active, gave her encouragement by laughing loudly.

In my friendliest tone, I asked the least active girl nearest to me, 'What's your name then?'

She yelled, 'Sarah!' then laughed out loud.

I decided to move to a position that would block the path of the baseball-cap wearer, which had the desired effect but caused another girl to shout aggressively:

'Leave Cheryl alone, or you'll be sorry!'

With my pulse accelerating more than I liked, I calmly but authoritatively suggested, 'Why don't we all sit down and have a chat?'

Sarah, surprisingly, seemed to respond to my suggestion by announcing, 'Come on, Kim.' (Kim, from the start, had been blocking Mirain from entering any further into the room.) 'Why don't we all sit down and have a fucking chat?'

I should point out that a member of the hostel staff later told me that the word 'fucking' was the most common descriptive word used by the students and it wasn't always meant negatively, so I should just ignore it!

Then, before I had time to decide on my next tactic, they were all sitting down waiting for my reaction. Mirain, though, had decided to stay in the spot Kim had selected for her. I casually sat down, near enough to the girls to show my 'lack of fear' but closer to the door than they were, just in case I needed a speedy exit.

Staying in my seat, rather than reaching for my register, I politely introduced myself.

'Well, my name's Tom. Can you tell me your names again please?'

Their response was accompanied by pushing and shoving as well as bursts of hysterical laughter as each gave their name.

'Nicola.'

'I'm Kimberley.'

'Nadine.'

'Call me Cheryl.'

'It's fucking Sarah, isn't it, Tom?'

Then it clicked.

Smiling and laughing to myself, I joked back, 'So you're all clever as well as funny. I'm really impressed. I guess you girls are "Calling the Shots" then?'

This time the joke was shared by all. Well, except for Mirain who was still standing in her selected spot.

Three hours later, my first morning's lesson was over and the girls seemed to have taken to me – I think. Very little teaching and learning had taken place, but far more importantly there had been no incidents – well, not ones that would be recorded at Ysgol Abaty at least!

Soon it was one o'clock and I waited anxiously for my afternoon class to arrive. Being a former Cub Scout, I told myself to *be prepared*. I took a deep breath and after another quick glance at the hole in the plasterboard, the door burst open again and in they came.

Five Key Stage 4 girls and one adult this time, and within a moment their presence filled the room. My only thoughts were, *These are even more confident and even bigger!*

Then a calm voice reassured me, 'Hiya, my name's Helen, and these are my lovely girls.'

As they gave their names, I noted that there was no Emma, Geri, or Victoria, and there wasn't even one Mel. Things were looking up!

Four hours into my teaching day and, with Helen's help, I was actually working through a planned lesson – well, sort of. Even with a group as cooperative as this one, the pace of the lesson was slow. I was frequently taken away from the content of the lesson, often for additional instruction due to surprising gaps in their knowledge rather than their intelligence, but also for informal conversations which they enjoyed.

Although the afternoon hadn't been as nerve-racking as the morning, where I was urging the clock onwards to the end of the lesson, I could feel the tension of the day in my shoulders. Then I suddenly noticed it was 3:18pm, only two minutes to go before I could ask them to tidy up and there had been no real issues.

Then it happened. Without warning, Bethan, the smallest girl in the class, stood up and walked out. No one seemed to pay any attention to her except me.

I asked Helen, 'Does Bethan often just get up and leave like that?'

'More often than I'd like, to tell the truth, but it's usually best not to challenge her. You've done well, Tom, keeping her here this long.' Seeing my puzzled look, she added, 'Bethan usually leaves halfway through the afternoon. Patience isn't one of her strong points.'

'Does she ever cause any problems in class?' I asked.

'Not often, but that hole by the door you look at every now and then... well, it was Bethan who put it there when she headbutted the wall.'

Working in an environment I was unaccustomed to, by 4:00pm I was already ready to go home, let alone work for another five hours plus!

The hostel work took me completely by surprise, as it didn't seem to be a continuation of the day job at all. Even the hostel's appearance was different. Looking at its façade, it reminded me of the simplicity of a young child's drawing of a house, whereas the school building, with its Victorian architecture, had ornate gables, coloured brickwork and detailed chimneys which demanded that you look up at them.

The same youngsters who'd had me sweating and working flat out to keep them on task and out of mischief during the day were suddenly friendly! I was hearing, 'Hi, Tom', 'Alright mate?' and other cordial greetings from everywhere I went. Some were even standing up and shaking me by the hand as a sign of welcome.

The students showed me around their hostel, including the recreation rooms, eating areas and even their personal spaces. They competed with each other to sit by me at dinner, and when they parted for their different activities, I was made welcome to join in any of these by the students themselves.

The menu of that first meal at Ysgol Abaty is crystal clear in my memory:

Starter
Chicken Liver Pate

Main
Roast rump of beef, carrots, cabbage, roast potatoes, Yorkshire pudding & gravy

Dessert
Sticky Toffee and Date Pudding, with Toffee sauce and Banana ice cream

As soon as you entered the dining room, you knew instantly that the food about to be served was going to be excellent. The aroma of favourite Sunday roasts greeted me and took me back to my mother's Sunday dinners with my father, mother, sisters and brother all sitting around the table in the kitchen. Then, no one could leave the table until everyone had finished, and puddings were only allowed if you'd eaten your entire main course. Pen-y-Bryn's meal was absolutely delicious in every way. I'd happily have paid 'top dollar' for it in any one of the many excellent restaurants that exist throughout North Wales and Cheshire.

The whole of the dining room was full of activity. Surprisingly to me, there was an orderly line of students waiting to be served their meals. I found out that, at meal times, the canteen ladies were the 'top dogs', no doubt because of the wondrous meals they produced. Students and staff treated them with nothing but respect, and deservedly so. 'Please', 'thank you' and '*diolch*' (the Welsh for 'thank you') were heard all around as the students collected and returned their plates. The students had quickly discovered that some Welsh words shared with the Welsh speaking canteen ladies usually paid dividends in the way of generous helpings.

Several of the hostel staff were sitting with the students enjoying their meals, though Mirain, who had told me during the first lesson that she'd be working in the hostel, was nowhere to be seen. When I asked a member of staff where she was, they quickly explained:

'Oh, her? She finished at the end of school saying we were to take her off our supply list. Happens all the time, and leaves us short-staffed.'

Tables and chairs, once neatly organised, were now spread around, like sheep scattered on a Welsh hillside, with no clue given as to their original location. Students sitting at the same table had started their meals at different times, resulting in various courses being consumed simultaneously. The one constant factor in all of this was the lack of waste on the plates. If local farmers were still collecting the 'slops' to feed to their pigs, as they did in my primary school days, they shouldn't waste any fuel collecting any from here.

At frequent intervals during the meal, the tranquillity would be broken by different students who took it in turns to draw attention of themselves. To a casual observer, this might be seen as amusing; to a new teacher and part-time member of the hostel staff, the manner in which they were doing this was simply scary!

On this evening (and as I found out, this was often the case), the most frequent attention-seeker was Colin. At just thirteen years old and pint-sized compared to the other students of his age, he appeared to be far too loud and confident. In most other environments, Colin would easily have drawn all of my attention to himself. In the dining room of Pen-y-Bryn, though, he had to compete with several others for pole position. I hadn't had the pleasure of teaching Colin yet. But it was Colin who had, in his own way, introduced me to the reality of teaching at Ysgol Abaty, for he was the mysterious white ninja I'd seen ten hours earlier on the roof. Then, I'd puzzled over his whereabouts for the next hour and twenty-five minutes. The solution was revealed when I attended the morning staff briefing, the hostel staff members also being present. Once the obligatory 'Welcome back' or *Croeso* had been said, Colin was the first student to be discussed.

'You'll hear Colin's name a lot in staff meetings,' whispered the young woman sitting on my left as she carefully placed her motorcycle helmet under her chair.

As I made a mental note to remember Colin's name and look for it on my class lists, one of the hostel staff explained to us that Colin hadn't been keen on returning to school, and had showed his displeasure by causing one incident after another on the hostel site early that morning. Two members of staff from the hostel had brought him to the school site before the start of the day, keen to avoid the 'domino effect' of other students copying Colin's antics. Although this had got him away from the hostel site, Colin wasn't happy about being at school far earlier than his fellow pupils. Following a game of 'cat and mouse' through the maze of corridors and classrooms, he'd even gone as far as shouting and singing to them from different locations around the school, if they lost sight of him for any length of time. I was later to learn that his rendition of 'Delilah' was a favourite tactic of his to draw attention to himself. He'd finally made his bid for freedom through an upstairs window – the scene I'd witnessed. Once on the roof, he'd run the length of the school, descending down a drain pipe and disappearing into the Strand Woods. He wasn't seen again until it was time for him to catch the minibus back to the hostel at the end of the school day. Hunger, as well as the cold and wet, had got the better of his bid for complete freedom.

At just four foot six inches tall, Colin easily made up for his lack of physical presence with the volume of his voice and his total lack of awareness of anyone else's personal space. He was spending more time standing up, wandering around and talking than he was actually eating. At regular intervals, his loud laugh would catch my attention, even when he was on the other side of the dining room. This greatly irritated the other students and staff who were trying to enjoy their meals. Colin had a strong South Walian accent, typical of the Welsh Valleys, and this was being mimicked by some of his peers, much to his annoyance. One older student called Joe seemed to have the South Walian accent off to a tee. Every time Colin came near to where Joe was sitting, Joe's automatic, 'What's occurring, boyo?' would cause the others much amusement. Yet Colin's shoulder-length blond hair and beaming smile would have made him a photographer's dream – if they could only keep him still and quiet.

Most of the students in the dining room were already known to me from my day's activities. A few I'd taught or, at least, had in my class when I was teaching. It was during dessert that I noticed Eve for the second time. I'd learned from Colin, on one of his recces over to where I was sitting, that she was the oldest student in *Wordsworth*, my own form. I hadn't met her yet as she'd been visiting local high schools to try to set up a part-time timetable with them.

Getting this information from Colin was hard work – not because he was secretive (if anything, Colin was the opposite), but because as he was having a conversation with you, he'd be on the move all the time. At the start of a sentence, he was sitting on your left. By the end of it, he was on your right. Then, in a flash, he was at the head of the table, standing up, and before he'd finished talking, he was off to another area of the dining room altogether.

A decision had been made by the Governing Board to give the classes' names rather than numbers. Not only that, but names of 'Great Britons'. The idea was to inspire the students, both socially and academically. So, on my timetable, I had two KS4 classes named *Wordsworth* and *Shakespeare,* and two KS3 classes named *Wren* and *Newton*. And not a single female role model among them! Where do governors get these ideas from? Soppy old Hollywood films, presumably! They obviously wanted a quick finish to their meeting, as not much thought had actually been put into the names. Any fan of television quiz shows would notice straight away that all the great British names they'd purposively considered at length were actually the same ones that appeared on British bank notes at the time. Perhaps they'd just looked in their wallets or purses!

I'd first noticed Eve about an hour and a half earlier, through the side window of the school workshop, when I'd presumed she was a member of staff. The workshop was to be my base for the practical lessons that I'd teach. Under the title 'Design and Technology', I'd been given far more freedom than in a mainstream school, and could adjust the curriculum to the students' needs in whatever way I saw fit. The chance to prepare individual lessons, and tidy up at the end of each one, didn't arise during the day at Ysgol Abaty. So, I'd decided straight away to spend some time after my last lesson of each day clearing up any mess that had been made and preparing for the following day's onslaught. It also gave me time to let the events of the day fade and to unwind before I drove home. Eve had run past the workshop on her way to Berwyn House, which was part of Pen-y-Bryn Hostel. This was almost an everyday occurrence for her, as I was to discover later.

All but three of the secondary students attending Ysgol Abaty, at least while I was working there, also attended Pen-y-Bryn. The hostel itself was divided into three sections called houses. These were named *Aran*, *Berwyn* and *Clwyd* after a mountain or range of mountains in north-east Wales – presumably to make remembering the hostel names as easy as A B C!

All around the dining room were individuals I'd get to know distinctly over my time at Ysgol Abaty. As well as staff members, I was noticing Colin, Roy, Eve, Martin, Peter, Dan, Chris, Stephen, Michael and Sean (AKA Yorkie). Not forgetting, of course, Priya and Bethan. For different reasons, all of them will have a unique and special place in my recollections.

Although I was born and bred in Greenfield, while teaching at Ysgol Abaty I lived in a little village on the outskirts of an old market town, which was about eighteen miles away. At the end of my first day of working at the school, I got back home at 9:31pm. I was more tired than I could ever remember being before, both physically and mentally. Even in my early days of marriage, when I had three jobs to make ends meet, I still had time for other activities besides work and sleep. Now these two activities seemed to fill my whole life. And as I settled down to sleep on that first night after teaching at Ysgol Abaty, the thought of my alarm going off at 6:10am to go back and do it all over again, wasn't very inviting.

The term 'steep learning curve' truly applied to my first few weeks at the school. The list of Special Educational Needs was a long and varied one; although the school had 'Communication and Interaction' noted as its speciality, many other special needs could be observed when working with the students. Some, such as ADHD[4] and Epilepsy, were plain to see at times. Others, for example, Autism and related disorders and Dyslexia, had been hidden and were still being hidden, if they could be, by many of the students.

In common with all other schools, paperwork was the bane of my life at Ysgol Abaty. It would be easy today for any teacher to spend more time doing paperwork than actual teaching. In a special school, though, the amount of paperwork is extreme. Filing cabinets can be bursting at their welded joints, containing folders full of files recording endless information about a student's history. With a school roll of forty-eight students, all with a statement of Special Educational Needs, Ysgol Abaty needed many filing cabinets.

The folders and files would give you all the background information that any social worker could ever want. But, to get the information you really needed to know about the students at this school, you had to talk to a member of the hostel staff or one of the LSAs. These were men and women from a wide range of backgrounds, including some from other care facilities; some were young and fresh, straight out of school, while others were older and more experienced, with varied professional backgrounds.

I'd first met my new colleagues socially when I'd attended their end-of-year summer party, prior to this autumn term. Not knowing what to expect, I'd left the pedestrian area of Holywell High Street and walked into a building that I remembered from my childhood as being Woolworths. This once common retailer had been replaced by 'The Market Cross', one of the many pubs in the Wetherspoon's chain. As well presented and welcoming as the environment was, I couldn't help feeling nostalgic about the many trips I'd made to 'Woollies' in my younger days. Whether it was doing the shopping for my mother or spending my pocket money on a paper bag full of broken biscuits for just two 'old' pennies.

Scanning the crowded pub for familiar faces, I saw the Deputy Head of Ysgol Abaty, David Davies, amidst a group of superheroes! As I snaked my way through the crowded room, it was easy to conclude that it was going to be an interesting evening. I circumnavigated my way around a six foot eight Viking (appearing over seven feet high with his horns!) in order to shake Mr Davies by the hand.

'*Ti'n iawn, boyo*? Call me Dai, everyone does,' was his

friendly welcome as he squeezed my hand tightly.

My automatic reply was, 'Thank you... Dai, it's great to meet you again.' I wondered what on earth I'd let myself in for. Another member of staff was dressed as Superman.

Leaning towards me, Superman confided, 'Hiya, I'm Simon by the way.' He nodded in Dai's direction and added, 'Everyone calls him Dai Twice,' as he also shook me by the hand. I discovered that Simon was a member of the hostel staff and I later learned just how appropriate his alter ego Superman really was.

I was made aware, later that evening, that when Dai Twice had been teaching secondary students Algebra in his first teaching post, they'd come up with his nickname: $a \times a = aa$, or 'a squared', which is known as 'a twice'. It was an easy step then for David Davies to become 'Dai Twice', and it had stuck. I also found it curious that Superman had decided to wear one of those costumes that came with padding to enhance muscle definition, when the padding was covering considerable natural muscle definition in the first place. Among the others gathered around me, I could easily pick out a Wonder Woman lookalike, as well as Elsa from *Frozen*.

The morning after the end-of-year party, having been up all night, I was sat among my new colleagues having breakfast in the McDonald's just off the A55 by the Caerwys junction. The previous twelve hours had led me to the conclusion that those weary people now sharing a fast-food breakfast with me were going to become very good friends.

Each of the students at Ysgol Abaty had a 'key worker'. Five minutes of conversation with any of them would enlighten you about any student you cared to mention. One of the key workers even warned me of the dangers of reading some of the information in the students' files. She explained, as we sat together during one of the break times having coffee, that knowing about some of the students' actions could lessen your chances of having a positive relationship with them.

'It's far better to treat them as you find them,' she said and smiled.

As I later read through some of the files that were necessary for my role at the school, it was easy to see what had brought her to this experienced conclusion. It was difficult to remove some of the students' appalling actions from my thoughts so that I could still consider them, and treat them, as children.

Rhiannon, a student who attended the school for less than a week, was a true paradox. She'd been transferred to Ysgol Abaty as an emergency placement and little in the way of paperwork had arrived with her. Dai Twice had spoken briefly with me during the Tuesday morning break before she arrived with the rest of the girls from *Wordsworth* in the afternoon.

'Generally, she's no problem at all, but you have to watch her,' was how Dai Twice put it. Though the doubt in his eyes as he quickly made an exit from the staffroom was slightly worrying.

As advised, I watched Rhiannon with considerable attention. Throughout the lesson she was polite and respectful, never raising any concerns for me. She even gave me a cheerful, 'Thanks, Tom, see ya later,' as she left the workshop. It seemed to me that the 'treat them as you find them advice' was appropriate.

My evening duty had consisted of chatting to various groups of students and watching snippets of *Two and a Half Men* which was on every time I visited the common room. As far as I was concerned, it was a relaxed, uneventful evening.

It was only when Susan beckoned me into her receptionist's office the following morning that I learned of the calamity of the previous night.

'Have you heard about last night?' she quizzed.

My vacant expression gave my answer as she continued.

'After lights out, Rhiannon sneaked out for a fag by the minibuses. Emma found her but she carried on, defiantly puffing away.'

A puzzled look on my face gained additional information.

'You won't know Emma; she's new in the hostel and was at the youth club with some of the girls last night until after you went home.' Susan continued, 'Well, apparently when Emma approached Rhiannon – in a "professional but placid way", according to Simon who was behind her – she started to coax her back into the hostel. Before Emma could do anything, though, Rhiannon had produced a knife and managed to cut Emma on the hand as she put her hand up to defend herself! Simon managed to get the knife off her as she tried to stab him too!'

With apprehension, I enquired, 'Are they OK? Where are Rhiannon and Emma now? God, Rhiannon was only in the workshop with me yesterday with "sharps" all over the place. I never thought for a minute she might stab someone!'

Susan concluded, 'The police were called and Rhiannon was taken to Holywell Police Station. Emma phoned this morning and told me to tell Dai Twice that she's OK, but she won't be coming back to work at the hostel again. Apparently, there's been a management meeting and it's been decided that Rhiannon isn't coming back either.'

I walked away shaking my head and, as I entered the workshop, I thought of all the 'sharps' that were on hand. That's when I decided to put the reading of students' files higher up on my list of priorities.

Chapter Three
Feeling Settled In

It was October, and I was already four weeks into my new job. Most importantly, I was feeling comfortable in both the school and the hostel. The time I'd spent socialising with the students during my hostel duties had paid off. My own form in particular had taken to me, it seemed. I'd also realised that, no matter how detailed your educational plans are, no teaching or learning can be successful without first forming positive relationships with the students. The educational content of the lesson (for example, the names of different tools and how to use them safely, how to correctly produce finished articles, etc.) had to come later – if at all!

It was just as well I was feeling more confident as the additional LSAs who'd arrived with some of my more difficult classes during my first week had been there for a 'honeymoon period' only, and now they'd been directed to more pressing priorities in the school. The management structure of the school allowed me to get on with teaching in my own way with little interference, which is certainly not the case in most schools where they're far more concerned with planning – long, mid and short-term.

Each Tuesday, as I tidied up my workshop at the end of the school day before setting off for my hostel shift, I'd notice Eve running past the window. Not only was Eve the oldest of the girls in *Wordsworth*, she was also the oldest student in the school, as Colin had informed me correctly, but wasn't until Dai Twice mentioned it at a staff meeting that I discovered she was nearly eighteen years old. Eve, who was thought of highly by all at Ysgol Abaty, had decided to repeat Key Stage 4 in order to gain additional qualifications. Not only did she attend her Ysgol Abaty classes, but she also spent time at some of the local high schools that were within reasonable travelling time, to improve her academic standards and social-interaction skills. Dave Littler was head of the hostel and should not be confused with Dai Twice. Being introduced to Dave Littler for the first time had been a memorable event. Meeting him, as I had in Wetherspoons in Holywell on my first staff night out, was made even more unforgettable by his presence as a six foot eight Viking. Simon had made a point of introducing me to as many members of staff as possible, adding in every case their friendly byname, if they had one. Of Dave Littler he'd said, 'That's Dave Littler, and everyone, in true Robin Hood tradition, calls him Little Dave.'

During the quieter periods at the hostel, Little Dave made a point of supporting new staff by discussing with them many of the characteristics of Special Educational Needs; he had a wealth of knowledge on the subject. He was the one who'd told me that Eve, one of the few students in Ysgol Abaty with Autism, had been given her statement at the end of her first year in secondary school. Having survived the cosy primary school environment, the greater social demands of a secondary school meant that before the end of Year 9, she'd completed her transition to Ysgol Abaty. The National Autistic Society statistics suggest that Autism affects only one girl to every eight boys, and within the school, the population with a statement of Autism did seem to reflect this statistic.

I'd first taught *Wordsworth*, excluding Eve, for Design and Technology on my first Tuesday afternoon. I'd been pleasantly surprised at how easy the students were to teach, as on that occasion they'd all appeared keen to learn and quite intelligent. Even Bethan, who didn't stay till the end of the lesson, had worked well while she was there. I'd spent a lot of the lesson wondering why they weren't in their own local high schools. When Eve had joined the class on Wednesday morning for their English lesson, she'd fitted this image perfectly, not appearing out of the ordinary in any way at all. She would have blended in easily at any high school, and I would have thought she'd have been very popular too. Tall at 1.78 metres (or five foot ten inches in 'old money', as my mother used to say), she was well above the average British woman's height of 1.6 metres. She had straight, ash-blonde hair, falling onto her shoulders – a colour many women would have wanted to purchase at their local chemist shop – and she had a smile, though rarely seen, that showed perfect ivory-white teeth, similar to the nameless smiles that fill the front covers of nearly every women's magazine. It didn't take me long to discover the magic formula as to why *Wordsworth*, including Eve, were so enjoyable to teach. The magic formula was the female LSA, Helen, who accompanied them everywhere and made my first afternoon so enjoyable and rewarding. There were seven others in the class, as well as Eve, who between them ticked most of the areas on the Special Needs range. But together, they seemed to balance each other out – at least for me... most of the time.

The class I taught each Thursday morning for Design and Technology were the opposite of *Wordsworth*. *Shakespeare* always arrived with three male LSAs. Together the LSAs added up to over three hundred kilograms of weight. I was frequently informed by one of the LSAs, on arrival, that at least one of the class had had a difficult morning. It was usually only 8.56am when they arrived! This was the earliest the hostel staff members could deliver them, without being told bluntly, 'You're too early.'

I spent all of September and October trying to keep *Shakespeare*'s 'collateral damage' to a minimum. They often wandered around, competing with each other to be as disruptive as possible, and it seemed that it was only during the last ten minutes of any of the lessons that I achieved any real communication with them. I should point out that I was chatting to them about current affairs.

ESTYN inspectors (the Welsh equivalent of OFSTED), please note that lesson plans, which you scrutinise so closely, were, and are, only a guide and often have to be ignored with students like these. With these students, it's seat-of-the-pants teaching or you don't survive.

During my second meal in Pen-y-Bryn Hostel, I recalled that Eve had sat at the same table as Helen and me. Helen, like many of the teaching assistants, also worked in the hostel. They seemed to chat to each other easily. All the tables, laid out for eight people, fitted in the old hall at Pen-y-Bryn perfectly. As with many rural houses, Pen-y-Bryn was far too big to be a modern home and far too undersized to be used as a special school or nursing home in its own right. Thirty years earlier, the idea of placing children with special educational needs in what were then cheap, large rural houses, no longer suitable for the nuclear family with its 2.4 children, had been all the rage.

The school rooms also had the same shortcomings, of course. With large, single-glazed windows filling most of the walls, there were cold spots throughout the school in winter and hot areas in summer. Looking around now, apart from the original dining area at the back of the building, it was difficult to work out whether the other rooms were too big or too small for their current use as classrooms. Ceilings were high enough to have large, brightly coloured Chinese kites (created by the 'artist in residence') hanging from them without fear of getting any head injuries. Yet there was no floor space for tables and chairs, which the students needed to use during their lessons.

When not teaching in the workshop, I spent much of my time organising the available furniture there – as in the children's sliding puzzle game, where you move blocks around in a frame to make a picture, discovering that each time you move one block into place, all the others consequently move to a poorer position. Helen was an expert at deciding on the best place to sit students during their lessons. With her help, I quickly learned that finding out which students could sit next to each other was crucial for any successful lesson to take place. This was especially true when teaching *Shakespeare* and *Wren*; then it became the Ysgol Abaty equivalent of trying to solve a Rubik's cube.

Teaching *Wordsworth* and then *Shakespeare* each Wednesday for English made me think of them as 'Yin and Yang' lessons. Yin in the morning and Yang in the afternoon, or perhaps it was the other way around? Chinese philosophy would have *Shakespeare* representing the male 'Yang' positive energy and *Wordsworth* the female 'Yin' negative energy. What was true, though, is that between them, their opposite yet complimentary energy involved all that is wonderful about teaching and learning.

Having completed the required practical tasks necessary to survive, I was now finding time to learn about all the special needs categories that can appear on an educational statement. Autism is by far the most complicated and varied of these. The term 'ASD' is used more commonly now – Autistic Spectrum Disorder. The word 'spectrum' is used as it is when speaking of light, suggesting the widest range of characteristics that those with Autism can display. Often classes would turn up with students missing from them. Reasons would include: not well, did not return after a home visit, meetings (there were so many meetings!), court appearance and sometimes simply 'did not want to go to school'. Even when at school, some students would miss lessons given by certain teachers, or certain subjects, out of their school day.

As well as Eve, a limited number of other students attended some of the local high schools. This was a very successful partnership between all the schools involved. In particular, it benefitted the Ysgol Abaty students as they were able to achieve nationally accredited examination qualifications such as GCSEs which weren't available at Ysgol Abaty. But I believe that many of the high school students also benefitted from the presence of the Ysgol Abaty students.

Even though I was settling in well, it was easy to see why the previous Design and Technology teacher had walked out one afternoon, never to return. *Shakespeare* alone could have this effect on a teacher. Imagine having eight fourteen, fifteen or sixteen year old lads in your class, some of whom were well known to (and had little or no respect for) the police in their local areas, as well as in North Wales. One or two were literally just killing time until they were to 'go down', after their next appearance in court. One such character was Alan from

Newcastle. Every time I hear 'Newcastle' voiced, I hear it in Alan's strong Geordie accent.

Like Eve, Alan was a unique character – as, of course, we all are. All of the staff members were pleased to meet him when he was being shown around by Dai Twice, and his description quickly spread throughout the school. Comments such as, 'I hope he decides to take the job', 'He's just what we need' and 'I need him as my assistant' were being shared among the staff.

The reason was simple: Alan was six foot tall and weighed seventeen stone, and none of it was fat! Consequently, some of the existing staff members thought he was a potential new member of staff, coming to strengthen the ranks.

It was during the afternoon staff briefing that Gareth Lee, our head teacher, clarified the situation to all of us, having heard the rumours.

'Alan's not a new member of staff; he'll be joining *Shakespeare* soon.' Then he added, 'He's been used as "muscle" by one of the "firms" in Newcastle, and he's ended up upsetting the wrong people. So, as well as educational reasons, he's been moved from the North East for his own safety.' Seeing the looks of disbelief on the faces of the staff, Gareth concluded, 'He's intelligent, but the poor lad has had little schooling. But not to worry; I have every faith in you all!'

Although he'd just turned fourteen years old, Alan was to be placed in *Shakespeare* as it seemed a better fit for him. Before leaving the meeting, Helen (my LSA with *Wordsworth*, who'd become as invaluable as my right hand) and I quickly decided that Alan was a student we were going to get along with.

One of the positive points about working at Ysgol Abaty was that teachers were left, in the main, to sort out the practicalities of their school day themselves. This allowed Alice, the Cookery (sorry, Domestic Science. No, sorry, Food Hygiene. Sorry, I give up!) teacher and I to adjust our timetables if we wished. So when I had a non-teaching lesson and Alice was timetabled to teach *Shakespeare* or *Wordsworth*, or vice versa, we could split *Shakespeare* and *Wordsworth* between us. It meant that we'd have less non-contact time, but it also meant that we had four students instead of eight, and we could also share the four LSAs as we thought best.

One of the tasks I'd set out to complete as quickly as possible was organising the workshop. A common problem was that some students had been wrecking other students' work. I decided that each class would have to have a locked cupboard of its own. At least this would mean that I could control access to the students' pieces of work. With no budget for this, I'd built a row of cupboards similar to kitchen base units, using twenty-five millimetre thick plywood donated to the school by a local timber yard, Coastal Wood Products. With the bases made, I still needed a worktop to finish them off. I'd learned that most of the staff would resist taking their students out of the school grounds. But a few, including Alice and Helen, had explained that, in reality, if you took the chance, it nearly always paid dividends in future lessons, as your relationship with the students became far stronger. Encouraged by this, I decided to take my half of *Shakespeare* to the local B&Q store to get a worktop for my row of newly constructed cupboards.

Confident of my ability to manage my selected half of *Shakespeare,* and with Alice's advice in mind, I volunteered to take Colin as well.

Alice had informed me, 'No one wants to take Colin out with them, but he really appreciates it, Tom, and he's usually as good as gold for me.'

Having Colin join me on the outing was quickly agreed to by Dai Twice, who was timetabled to teach *Wren* for History.

'*Dim problem*! You keep Colin for as long as you need him, boyo,' was how he put it, as a broad smile spread across his face.

I got the feeling that Dai Twice wanted me to keep Colin for the rest of the day, if not the week!

I'd learned that the practice of mixing up class members was common at Ysgol Abaty. Usually it was at short notice to avoid any disruption or incident, but also, as on this occasion with Colin, it was to build bonds and reward positive progress. Perhaps I should have explained that most of the practical-based lessons lasted either all morning or all afternoon. Needless to say, the students never hurried back after their morning or afternoon outings.

The good news was that when I arrived at B&Q just outside Rhyl, there was a special offer on the four-metre-long worktops. This was a little more than I needed but was ideal as I could complete the existing cupboards and have an additional work surface to enable me to spread the students out even more and increase the 'out-of-kicking/punching' distance. The bad news was that Roy, an avid football supporter from Liverpool, who was wearing one of his many Everton shirts, couldn't lift it with me. Although he was one of the older and fitter lads, he was determined that none of the dust from the worktop would make his new shirt dirty, and his awkward stance combined with his good sense of humour had us both laughing at our feeble attempts to lift it. Then along came big 'Big Al' as all the students referred to him.

'Am choking forra cuppa, man. Can we gan now?' He quickly picked it up single-handedly and headed off to one of the tills.

Alan is definitely a student just made for staff to get along with… if I can only get past the language barrier, I thought.

The only problem during the outing was when Colin saw Alan picking up the worktop so easily and in response exclaimed, 'Fucking hell!' louder than I would have liked in the crowded store.

Feeling obliged to respond to his outburst, I reacted with, 'Colin, shush! Remember we're on our best behaviour.'

Although I corrected Colin on his language, I deliberately made little fuss about it. After all, I was thinking exactly the same thing.

Settling into a new job always takes time, but Ysgol Abaty had the sort of environment that, no matter how long they'd been there, some teachers would never quite settle. However, somehow, on some days, I truly felt relaxed and comfortable. On this particular week, it was made stranger by the fact that other schools were having their half-term break. As already explained, Ysgol Abaty, as a private school, had chosen to have a school term made up of a maximum of five working weeks, and occasionally only four, and then one week's holiday. This meant that I'd already had my first autumn-term holiday and was looking forward to my second week off before the end of the term. Having got used to the idea, and taken advantage of the lower cost of holiday prices, I was all in favour of the system. This Tuesday was my first relaxed one. Well, not really relaxed, but close to it. In the afternoon, Alice and I decided to team-teach *Wordsworth* as Alice had one of her two non-teaching afternoons. I really enjoyed teaching alongside her and eating the wonderful food she produced with the students in the Cookery Room.

Later on, as I sat down to have my evening meal in Pen-y-Bryn, Eve and another student, Priya, came in and sat down beside me. Eve and Priya were great friends. They'd been in *Wordsworth* for the longest time, so usually when you saw one, you saw the other. Although I'd taught both girls several times, this was the first occasion I'd spent time with them in a less formal setting. As I chatted away, I provided them with a few snippets of information about myself. This is a technique that I'd later include in my list of skills for students to acquire. I was already realising that many of the students at Ysgol

Abaty didn't recognise or practise appropriate exchanges when meeting people.

Priya, whose appearance when I first saw her instantly reminded me of Jess, the character played by Parminder Nagra in the 2002 film *Bend It Like Beckham*, listened intently to me, though responded only when directly asked a question. Eve, on the other hand, responded relentlessly. She disclosed her name, age, where she was from and why she was at the school. She'd acquired excellent English grammar and spoke with perfect diction. Just as I was wondering why she was here, it became evident.

Eve carried on with her supply of personal information without taking any note of my interest levels. And she was far too informative. It was as if she was reading out a list of bullet points on a personal information form or CV. I knew that certain facts should be kept secret or at least only divulged in confidence once a positive relationship had been developed. But within five minutes, and without any encouragement, I knew about her sister's Cystic Fibrosis, her parents' divorce and the reason for it. I knew how she felt about the staff members who worked with her, including their faults. All the information was correct, even the staffs' faults! But the freedom with which the information was given was somehow... wrong.

I decided to change the direction of the conversation. As I'd seen Eve running past the workshop a few times while I tidied up each day, I thought our mutual interest in running would work as a topic of interest.

'I used to be a keen runner. I still run a few times a week, but only for fitness, not competitively,' I began and smiled. 'Where and how often do you run, Eve? I presume Dai Twice is happy with you missing some afternoon lessons?' I'd assumed that she ran around the local woodland on her afternoon off as she made her way up to Pen-y-Bryn.

But she replied authoritatively, 'I have lessons in the afternoon; I never miss any of my lessons.'

Now I was puzzled, as she was immaculately turned out and had, in my opinion, showed no signs of having just finished a run, no matter how early I saw her at the start of my shift in Pen-y-Bryn. I decided to mention some of the areas where I ran and the routes I took. This allowed me to politely ask as a follow-up question:

'Where do you run each day, after school finishes?'

She sat up straight, leaned over and proclaimed, 'I run from school to Berwyn House every afternoon.'

The reality of life in a special school filled my thoughts. I knew that school finished at 3:30pm and that all the students had to attend the end-of-school briefing each day, which usually went on till about 3:45pm. I'd learned how to avoid getting caught up in the 'wagon train' of minibuses and cars going from school to the hostel by positioning myself next to the door, so that I was the first to get away. This meant that I was never late for hostel, as my shift started at 4:00pm. How was it that on three occasions, including today, Eve had run past my car as I was parking up? She'd also found time to change into her running gear!

Seeing the puzzled look on my face, Priya then entered into the conversation and for the first time, without a prompt, she said, 'Eve's great at running; she always wins.'

As I carried on with what could be called polite conversation with Eve and Priya, I realised I was, in fact, still assessing them. Not by giving them Jessop spelling age tests, National Curriculum levels or using any educational scheme, but by simply listening to them and seeing if I got on with them, which was pleasantly easy to do.

Eve said to me, 'When I leave here next year, I'm going to have a good job and live in my own flat without any help from anyone.'

Seeing the self-belief she had, I replied positively, 'That's a great plan. Do you know what job you want?'

She sat back in her chair and paused for thought. 'Not really, but I know I'm going to go abroad for holidays, I'm going to have lots of friends and I'm going to be happy.'

These are, of course, all the things that each one of us would want for ourselves.

As the small talk came to an end, Eve thought for a moment and then remarked with an air of confidence, 'Don't worry, Tom, Priya and I won't give you any problems in class; we just have relationship problems cos we're on the spectrum.'

Then they were gone, leaving me still puzzling over Eve's directness and her running ability.

*

Later the same evening, as it neared 8:30pm, both hostel staff and students gathered into small groups to enjoy a drink and some biscuits or toast, before the students went to their individual rooms for the night.

As Little Dave, Chris and Michael from *Wren,* and I were enjoying a hot chocolate, I mentioned Eve's running and probed further.

'How far does Eve run?' I asked.

Chris had spent most of his life moving from one care home or hostel to another, but had settled in well at Pen-y-Bryn. Michael was a gifted artist who had several of his paintings hung around the school and hostel. He'd also won some national prizes for his art. The three of them were able to tell me that Eve ran every day.

Little Dave said, 'Because of Eve's age and maturity, and because we know we can always trust her, she's allowed to go off by herself whenever she wants.' As Little Dave emphasised 'trust her', he took the opportunity to look directly at Chris and Michael. Then he added, 'None of the students or staff here can keep up with her anyway; even Simon who runs for a local harriers' club says she's out of his league!'

Chris chipped in with, 'Once she ran to Chester and back, you know.'

I knew from my younger days, when I went to the nightclubs in Chester from my home in Greenfield, that it was a distance of about eighteen miles.

'And it only took her half an hour!' Michael added.

On seeing my astonished face, Little Dave smiled knowingly and gave me a wink.

Little Dave admitted that he didn't really know much about Eve's running ability, and the boys continued to guess at the great distances and times she'd achieved, all of which seemed totally unrealistic. He did know how long she ran for, though, as Eve always notified a member of staff before she went out for a run and told them how long it would take her to do it. This information would then be recorded in the activities book. Eve's runs would take up to three hours sometimes. As to how fast she was, no one knew. Apart from the short distances she ran at high school, where she won all the races she entered, no one had ever timed her. Recollecting the film *Forrest Gump*, I remembered that when Forrest had decided to 'go for a little run' he'd ended up running across the country five times. I decided, there and then, that Eve's running was something I needed to investigate further.

It was pointless to carry on guessing at Eve's running speeds; what I needed to do was find a way of getting some statistics: routes, distances and times. I therefore decided to make the run from school to the hostel myself. Though not as fit as I'd like to be, I knew the route well and therefore the pace to set for myself. The following Saturday morning, I parked up at the Greenfield Heritage Park and did a rudimentary warm-up, which was always a practice of mine. It was an unusually warm October day, averaging between fifteen and seventeen degrees, there was little wind and no sign of rain, so near-perfect running conditions.

I waited till my watch displayed 10:30am exactly, in

case I messed up the stopwatch function while checking the time. I didn't want to have to repeat the run unnecessarily. I usually use an app on my phone, but out of nostalgia, I'd decided to use the old silver stopwatch my father had given me when I'd started my running in this area years earlier. The initial part of the route is ideal and is almost a warm-up in itself. But after the first few minutes, the terrain gets steeper and steeper. A careful path is needed to be taken through the pedestrians who can be found near the top of Well Hill, and safety has to be assessed as you pass over the Fron Park Road.

As I crossed the main road, a sudden whiff of car fumes brought back some childhood memories of the Pistyll Estate a short distance away. I'd always targeted this area during my 'Bob A Job' week – the places where the 'rich folk' lived. You'd often get a donation without actually doing a job. I know this wasn't in the true spirit of the scheme, but it made up for the times when you were sorry you'd bothered to knock on somebody's door.

I remember Wednesday, June 3rd 1964, when my friend Mark and I were asked to cut the front lawn of a house on the Pistyll Estate with a pair of scissors! The lady who lived there explained that her gardener was on holiday and that the grass had grown too long. In the spirit of the scheme, she'd given us a bob. The old bob or shilling would be the equivalent of five new pence these days. We also had to share it!

When I reflect on memories like this with my friends, I'm always puzzled by which is stranger: that I can remember specific events with their dates, or that they can't? When my eldest daughter Anneka was born, I didn't have to memorise the date; I just always knew it: 3rd October 1987. My friends also seemed to remember their own children's birth dates with very little difficulty. But why then do I know that Anneka's first day at school was Monday, 9th September 1991? But when I ask them when their children started school, the usual reply is, 'When he or she was three or four,' rather than the actual date. I wonder what they'd think of me if I answered their questions in a similar style:

'When was your daughter Anneka born, Tom?'

'When she was nothing!'

Once you're twenty-five metres up the Pen y Ball Hill, all you can think about is running. Looking at the road a metre or so ahead of you helps to remove the reality of how steep the hill actually is. On steep hill runs like this, I count paces or use a different arm action, anything to take my mind off the effort I have to put into it.

I paused briefly at the monument at the top, which was erected in 1893 to commemorate events in the life of King George V, and then, allowing a little further distance than the hostel gates, I stopped and checked my stopwatch. I backed up the recorded time by noting the time between start and finish on my phone: fifteen minutes, fifteen seconds.

I'd carried out an estimated time check on Eve's running time on Friday, when I'd stayed behind to chat to the hostel staff about events during the week. Eve had passed *Berwyn*'s entrance just after 4:00pm, two minutes past to be precise on the 'controlled clock' at the hostel.

(Controlled clocks were fitted throughout the school and hostel to make sure that no one could ever moan about having a class for too long or students arriving too early.) She had taken about seventeen minutes.

Impressive, I thought, with a touch of satisfaction that I'd achieved a quicker time. But then I remembered that she was in casual clothes at 3.45pm, and not in her running shorts and bright yellow vest, which she always wore to run. Eve had probably taken the time to change and even do a warm-up as well!

During that same week, I made a point of catching up with Paul, an old school friend, who also happened to be a PE teacher at one of the high schools that Eve attended part-time. Paul was a former pupil of The Ave Maria Boys' College in Chester. He was still playing competitive rugby for the 'old boys' and had also coached several track champions during his teaching career. He did know of Eve and knew that she opted to run whenever possible during any of the PE lessons that she joined in with. Otherwise, unfortunately, she'd just become a blur in the mass of students who didn't tend to catch your eye at high school. And as the high school athletics timetables had finished for the summer term, there was no opportunity to assess Eve through the school's programme.

I mentioned my knowledge of running and my possible expectations of Eve to Alice as she was getting some of the students from my class to help her carry supplies for her afternoon cookery lesson. She had a simple solution to finding out how good Eve was:

'If you really think she's that good, Tom, why don't you enter her into a race?'

I got back in touch with my friend Paul and he advised me that the 'Clogwyn Manod 10K' would be taking place at the beginning of next month. This was a popular North Wales competition, with all profits going to a local Search and Rescue Team who had their base not far from Ysgol Abaty. It was a challenging 10k distance, set in and around the beautiful lakes and forests that are to the north-east of Capel Curig in Snowdonia. Although it's not on the 'professional' circuit, it always attracts a lot of competitive runners. All I had to do now was ask Eve if she wanted to enter.

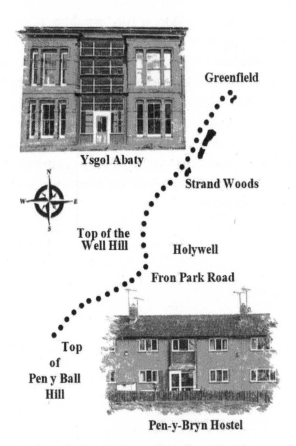

Greenfield

Ysgol Abaty

Strand Woods

Top of the
Well Hill

Holywell

Fron Park Road

Top
of
Pen y Ball
Hill

Pen-y-Bryn Hostel

Route 1: Ysgol Abaty to Pen-y-Bryn Hostel:
Approximately 3.2 kilometres
with 230 metres' height gain.

Chapter Four
The Clogwyn Manod 10k

'A friend has told me about a race called the Clogwyn Manod 10K,' I began, deciding to get straight to the point, 'I think you'd really enjoy it, Eve... What do you think about taking part?'

To my surprise, and without a hint of hesitation, she replied, 'Oh, yes please, Tom! When is it?'

Unexpectedly, she wasn't only willing to take part, she was enthusiastic about it too. None of the nerves that I assumed would be involved in such an idea were evident.

The race always took place on the first Sunday in November, so I had three weeks to prepare Eve for the event. Alice, who enjoyed most sports herself, was brought on board to look after her nutrition and to help with motivation. Alice's nutritional advice included a good breakfast, high in carbohydrates (approximately 700 kcals) but low in sugar, perhaps to include a banana (100 kcals), which Eve was to eat about three hours before the race. Also, as much toast and honey as she wanted – one of her favourites!

Alice's presence would also avoid complications with me spending time alone with Eve. A teacher spending time alone with a student, unfortunately, should be avoided wherever possible in these modern times. It's a sad reflection that support is now made difficult to provide when, in the past, support would have been given naturally by a teacher to a student without a second thought. This age of 'pre-planning', 'risk assessments', 'additional supervision' and the Disclosure and Barring Service (a merger of the Criminal Records Bureau and the Independent Safeguarding Authority), although having some merits may have removed many positive features of past times, including the possibility of spontaneous action.

Alice was taking her role very seriously and believing that all would go well in the Clogwyn Manod 10K, as well as now knowing the diary of race events in North Wales, Alice had already planned future training and racing diets, and was as keen to put her theories to the test as Eve was to enter races.

Eve, Alice and I were full of enthusiasm as we met up on the following Wednesday afternoon. Even after a busy school day, at exactly 3:50pm we were standing just inside the iron gates of Ysgol Abaty, considering the weather forecast for the next hour: cool and overcast with no rain. Those who have worked with young people diagnosed with Asperger's Syndrome (as Eve was), will know that the word 'prompt' can have two interpretations: either it would have no meaning at all to them, or they would always be accurate to the second. Luckily for Alice and me, Eve had the second understanding of the word.

The three of us set off from Ysgol Abaty's entrance, happy that the forecast was almost perfect for running. This was more of a social event than a training one and wasn't even part of my directed time. Setting off at roughly a five-minutes-per-kilometre pace, it was obvious even as we reached the mill pond three hundred metres from the school that Alice was struggling to keep up with me and Eve.

My suggestion of, 'Why don't we jog instead of run, so we can chat more?' must have seemed like music to Alice's ears. But even at Eve's 'jogging pace', I suggested that Alice turn back towards the school after a kilometre, and Eve and I would catch her up.

Another five minutes of running, and Eve and I also turned back towards school. As we did so, Eve asked:

'Can I run now, Tom?'

'Off you go then; I'll follow you,' I replied, smiling at her understanding of 'run'.

She was gone at a speed that took me by surprise, and one I was never going to match.

As I came through the school gates, Alice and Eve cheered loudly, emphasising that I was the last one back.

'How'd you get on?' I asked, looking at the two of them.

'Eve whisked past me by the mill pond,' was Alice's

reply.

Alice and I knew then that future runs would have to change in content. Eve had taken to the idea of training as I'd hoped she would – like a duck to water, or in this case, a greyhound to sprinting! Every aspect of the training was strictly adhered to over the following weeks. Alice had done all the research required to ensure that Eve's diet was as it should be. She'd also taken Eve to Chester to check out the best available running shoes, which took far longer than Alice had imagined as Eve was determined to find a particular colour.

'What do you think then, Eve?' Alice probed as, in the fourth sports shop they'd found, Eve tried on a bright yellow pair of trail shoes.

Eve stood up and rocked back and forth on the soles of her feet. 'These are just perfect,' she said to the sales assistant as she walked up and down the store, trying out the shoes.

'A yellow pair, Eve? What a surprise!' was Alice's tongue-in-cheek response.

Unless she was having her picture taken, Eve's natural expression tended to be a deadpan one. Alice later informed me that, as they had left the store, Eve, with her new shoes tucked tightly under her arm, had worn the happiest expression Alice had ever seen.

The approach to the race location, through Betws-y-Coed along the busy A5 road, must be as daunting as it is impressive to newcomers to the area. With each bend in the road, the gentle surrounding hills grow and grow until they become spectacular mountains. Arriving at 11:02am on the morning of the race, we parked up alongside the handful of cars that had arrived ahead of us, within sight of Cobden's Hotel on the A5. The early arrivals were spread out around us. Some were gathered in groups, chatting and laughing out loud, while others had found quiet spots to go through their individual warm-up routines or contemplate the race ahead of them. This was the ideal time to arrive; there would be no rushing about. There was plenty of time to register and to take in the stunning scenery around us. The atmosphere prior to the start of a race is always special, so the last thing I wanted was for Eve's nerves to get the better of her, especially considering her obsession with being on time for everything. We seemed to have that in common!

Slowly, the field set aside for parking filled up with vehicles until there was little room left and the latecomers had to spoil the lines of uniformly parked cars by squeezing in where they could. At the far side of the field, away from the road, two retailers of sports equipment had set up their stalls. One had a large gazebo with boxes of running gear laid out neatly. Here you could buy just about anything you needed from a host of sportswear manufacturers, and at budget prices. Eve couldn't control her urge to buy a bright yellow baseball cap hung up high on one of the stall's hooks. She made sure the cap matched the colour of her running shoes exactly, before slipping it onto her head.

'That'll make you easy to spot!' Alice laughed.

The other retailer was selling out of the back of his

Luton van. It was a well-known local manufacturer who, as well as running wear, had camping and mountain gear for sale, again at knock-down prices. I was sorry I didn't have more time to browse.

As Eve didn't have a heart-rate monitor to guide her pace, and it was a 10k cross-country course which she didn't know, I gave her the simplest but most important of all race tactics:

'Use your breathing to control your pace,' I said. Then, jokingly, I added, 'Only let two runners get ahead of you and then, if you can, when you're two hundred metres from the finish line, get into second place. When you think there's only one hundred metres left to go, overtake the person in front of you and stay there. It's simple, really!'

Alice smiled at Eve and then looked at me sternly. 'Tom, you do remember it's her first race, don't you!'

But Eve ended the discussion with, 'Don't worry, I know what to do. You two just need to relax.'

At 12:55pm, I gave Eve a banana, which was appropriate, according to Alice, bearing in mind the distance and rugged terrain of the race course. You'll see bananas being eaten by all the top sports athletes – often during the competition itself, if the opportunity is available. Think back to tennis star Andy Murray, before winning his Olympic Gold Medal in 2012.

To keep team spirits high, and to show empathy as well, Alice and I had a banana too. We were also starving, as we hadn't eaten since leaving Pen-y-Bryn Hostel about three hours earlier.

Alice and I encouraged Eve to make – in fact, push – her way to the front.

'Don't worry about anybody else or manners... get as near to the front as you can at the start,' said Alice, much to my surprise.

And Eve set out to do just that. Her apparent inability to recognise the personal space of others was a distinct advantage. We could see her making her way through the crowd of competitors until she was almost at the front. Then the sight of her ash-blonde ponytail tucked through her newly purchased yellow baseball cap disappeared into the kaleidoscope of colours that made up the runners. All we could do was hope that she was still jostling successfully with the other competitors for her desired starting position at, or near, the front.

The circular race was due to finish close to the replica stagecoach opposite the Tyn-y-Coed Inn, a short stroll away. So, as soon as the starter's air horn sounded, we made our way there, using the path beside Afon Llugwy. This would mean that we'd be standing around for a bit, but Alice and I wanted to be in Eve's sight as she neared the finish, if possible as we weren't sure how Eve would respond to not winning.

Even though we'd set off as soon as the air horn had sounded, we still had to do our own bit of nudging and pushing in order to find a vantage point about fifty metres before the finish tape. From here, we'd be able to see the runners coming straight towards us before they completed their final turn downhill to the finish.

*

The time was nearing 1:40pm when a group of spectators by the side of the course, just ahead of us, burst into cheering. We briefly saw the polychromatic running vests belonging to the front runners appear among the trees, before they disappeared again out of sight in the last hollow before the final ascent of the course. Then the first group of six came over the brow of the hill heading straight for us. At the front was the figure of a typical 'squaddie', perhaps from the local camp at Capel Curig. His vest and shorts had a tricolour design: a large black central panel separated from gold sides by a contrasting white line. Head held high and shoulders back, every pace he took suggested the raw power that was necessary on the battlefield. A large logo on his chest showed a flying Union Jack with the words 'Team Army' in bold print below it.

Four metres or so behind this squaddie was a red-shirted athlete who obviously wished the race had been nine and a half kilometres, rather than ten. His facial expression, and breathing, revealed to all that each step was being made with agonising effort; if the end hadn't been so close, then he would surely have eased off his rapid pace. But now, with the finishing line in sight, he had no choice but to keep on pounding away. The third-placed runner could well have been a clone of the first, the only difference being the black woolly hat that he wore. Looking over his shoulder as he ran, he was confident of his position.

About fifteen metres behind him, a second wave of three runners were about to determine their relative finishing positions, depending on the sprint finish they had left in them. The kaleidoscope of colours that we'd seen at the start was about to appear again, like a rainbow sparkling on the hillside. Red tops with black shorts, red tops with white shorts, green tops with red shorts; different combinations were everywhere.

A good race, I thought, as I was getting ready to add my voice to the cheers of the crowd for the front runners. Trying to pick out Eve would be more difficult, as the following groups of runners were clustered in larger numbers. I tried to wish Eve into view, but there was no sign of her in her favourite yellow running top as I scanned through the new runners just coming into view.

Then Alice grabbed my left arm. 'She's there! She's there!' she shouted hysterically.

I followed Alice's line of vision towards the very front runners. There, behind the first squaddie, like an aura of light down his right side, were the colours of Alice's running kit. She was wearing a bright yellow top (not a typical running vest, but a long-sleeved version similar to a winter thermal vest) and yellow tracksters, rather than shorts, with thin black piping down the outside of the legs. She was matching the front runner step for step, as if she was playing his shadow in an act from a vaudeville show.

'What?' I gasped, shocked. 'Never!'

As they approached us, Alice was deafening me as she jumped up and down and screamed, 'Come on, Eve! Keep with him! Go for it!' Her shouting was echoing around the valley – as well as my head!

As Eve passed us, separated from us by only a thin tape strung between posts, which marked the edge of the course, I could only scream out one word at the top of my voice, 'Go!'

Then, as if a switch had been flicked, Eve increased her pace, just as she had on the training run when I told her to leave me and go after Alice. Without altering her stride, she was level with the front squaddie within five paces, and then within another two she was in front. My mouth hung open and I couldn't breathe. Alice was trying to hold back tears.

Like Mo Farah in the 2012 5,000m Olympics final, Eve left the others in her wake. By the finish line, although still looking straight ahead, she was able to ease her pace. Eve hadn't only entered her first open competitive race, she'd won it, and won it in style.

Although it was a low-profile race, prizes had been donated by various companies and organisations across North Wales, which meant that Eve could choose from an excellent selection of goodies. With little surprise to Alice or me, Eve chose a rucksack for runners (complete with an internal Camelbak fluid carrier), not because of its high value, or its well-known designer make, not even so that she could easily extend her running distances or choice of routes; her reason was simple – it was yellow and black. To say that Alice and I were pleased doesn't even come close to it!

On the drive back to Pen-y-Bryn Hostel, we stopped off at one of the many wonderful cafés that can be found in the Snowdonia National Park. Eve was still in training mode, so she ordered pasta with brown rice and fresh orange juice to drink. Alice also went for a healthy option: butternut squash with chilli and crème fraiche. I had a 'Mega Breakfast' with a pint of tea – well, I'd had a stressful day! The most comical experience occurred as I was finishing my last piece of toast.

Alice asked the young waiter, who we later speculated was on his first day of employment there, 'Please could I have a bitter lemon to cool my mouth down after my chilli?'

'Certainly, madam,' was his well-mannered response.

Two minutes later, and on his own initiative, the youngster had returned with a side plate on which there was placed a single segment of lemon. He'd produced what he thought had been ordered.

As he set the saucer on the table at Alice's side, he politely said, 'Your bit of lemon, madam.'

Alice, not wanting to burst his bubble, replied cordially, 'Thank you, that's just what I wanted.'

As he walked off, Eve innocently asked the two of us, 'What's making you laugh so much?'

My first two classes on the following Monday morning contained little teaching and learning and didn't bear much resemblance to the timetable. What they did contain, in abundance, was pleasant socialising and, if I dare say it, 'bonding'. Everyone wanted to know if it was true that Eve had won the race.

'How fast was she?'

'Who did she beat?'

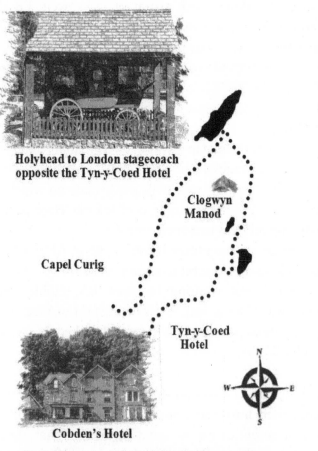

Holyhead to London stagecoach
opposite the Tyn-y-Coed Hotel

Clogwyn
Manod

Capel Curig

Tyn-y-Coed
Hotel

Cobden's Hotel

*Route 2: Clogwyn Manod 10K: 10 kilometres long
and approximately 300 metres' height gain.*

Priya even asked, 'Is Eve faster than you, Tom?'

'Of course; I'm old now and I've stopped training,' I said with a smile on my face.

She was faster than me when I was young and in full training, I thought to myself.

It was great to discover that Eve's first race was of common interest and a discussion topic for all. Although I tried lamely to execute the planned lessons that morning, I was as keen to tell them about Eve's achievement as they were to hear about it. Usually, you can't do anything but concentrate on the lesson in hand, and your chances of surviving it, when teaching at Ysgol Abaty, but today I was more preoccupied with the time on the clock. I was desperate to find out how Eve was, and to discuss what to do next with her and Alice. I wanted to get the laptop initialised (an American term meaning 'turned on'), so that I could search for every variation of race – cross-country, marathon, mountain, fell – that I could think of. I now needed a training plan! Sorry... Eve needed a training plan!

I had a 'working lunch' with Alice, Eve, Priya and a few others, including Martin and Peter (two of the boys from *Shakespeare*) and, to my surprise, Colin, who for once was sitting still and listening intently. Martin and Peter wanted to quiz Eve about every aspect of the race, but they lost momentum as Eve seemed to only give two replies, much to the boys' disappointment, which were either 'I ran faster' or 'They ran slower than me'.

Alice was more eager to know how Eve felt physically. I know all too well that it's usually the day after a race that the physical exertion has its effect, but Eve didn't seem to understand why Alice was even asking the question.

I was then able to spend my non-contact lesson that afternoon matching fixtures to dates in my year planner. Initially, it was completely out of balance; I'd entered every event possible within a realistic travelling distance of the school without realising just how many were available. But by deleting the ones further away from Ysgol Abaty, and selecting ones that stood out, I eventually achieved a doable schedule. I was pleased with my selection of events as they allowed for increased difficulty and were planned around training periods and rest days. And I now had the name of the next race: the Pensarn to Llandudno 16. This was ideal as Eve would have time to recover and prepare fully before competing again. It also gave me time to do some more research into my new role as 'personal coach and trainer', and to persuade Alice that she was going to add 'mentor and counsellor' to her existing role of dietician.

Unlike the Clogwyn Manod 10k circuit, the Pensarn to Llandudno 16 was run on a tarmac surface. Once a year, part of the Clwyd Bike Track is closed to cyclists, allowing the event to take place. The name of the race comes from the start and end locations on the course and, of course, the sixteen kilometre distance.

Alice and I had three main considerations. It was, in essence, a road race – the overall pace would be faster and more even than in a cross-country event. And I knew that Eve hadn't run a competitive sixteen kilometre race before. How would she perform in the second half of it? There would also be a large number of competitors, including some excellent club runners.

Leaving Alice to work on her areas of support, I decided that my first job was to enable Eve to develop an awareness of her own pace. She needed to know what pace she was doing and, when appropriate, how to maintain, increase or even decrease it. She'd never considered this. In the past, she'd let the terrain govern her pace or, in the case of the Clogwyn Manod 10k circuit, the other runners. From now on, Eve's training schedule would include longer distances at the weekend, with a rest day on a Monday – if I could persuade her to have one! So, tomorrow would be her first official training day.

As I discussed the schedule with Eve, she was full of enthusiasm. Determined to do her best, she found it difficult to understand why I didn't want her going out running again that evening. Her understanding was that the distance should increase day after day, until she was running the full sixteen kilometres. Then she would keep the same distance, but run it faster each day. However, I believe it's essential to include rest days in a training schedule. This doesn't necessarily mean not doing any exercise or running, but it does allow time for recovery and time for the muscles to strengthen and grow. It also allows time for any muscle damage to recover, or any potential damage to be avoided.

I took into account Eve's natural fitness, which had

obviously been enhanced by her long individual runs in the past but, even so, during the first week, Eve completed three 'easy run' days. And these were scheduled in addition to her run from school to the hostel. Now, being aware that Eve was crystalline and honest about where she'd run and how long it had taken, I set a distance of thirteen kilometres for the Wednesday and Friday evenings. By the end of the week, with all going far better than I'd hoped it would, I decided, after Eve had pointed out how easy my training runs were for her, to change from the planned fourteen kilometres to sixteen kilometres on the Sunday.

The second week was as easy as the first – at least it was for me! It was almost a repeat of the first week's training, except that the longer run was increased to nineteen kilometres. To my amazement, Eve still seemed to be taking it all in her stride. I'd now added a running watch to Eve's training accessories. With a bright yellow facial surround and strap, and with bold black numbers on a white dial, it was Eve's style to a tee. As a reward for Eve's success in the Clogwyn Manod 10k circuit, Alice and I had managed to persuade the powers that be at Pen-y-Bryn to give us some money to spend on Eve, and the watch had perfectly fitted the bill.

Eve could now check her individual kilometre times as she ran her routes. I'd completed each of the routes in my Fabia, and with the aid of 'Strava', I'd discreetly put a marker at each kilometre interval. Originally, I'd come across Strava, a fitness activity tracker app, when one of my friends had started listing his bicycling trips on

Facebook. He'd listed these trips under headings such as 'Cycled seventy-two kilometres with Strava'. With no knowledge of the app at the time, it was quite a while before I realised that he wasn't riding with a new friend from Greece.

As a training exercise in timing, I'd set Eve a six minute interval challenge. This required Eve to run a course that I'd tailored for her, near to Pen-y-Bryn. She should aim to finish as near to the six minutes as possible, rest for one minute, and then repeat the course again. She'd have to adjust her pace each time to be nearer to the six-minute target. This allowed her to concentrate on her timing ability and not on her stamina. The varied terrain would be the only complication. The two shorter runs were to be at five minute, thirty second intervals, and the third was to be a Fartlek session. An amusing fact, which all runners know, is that they will have flatulence at times – but this isn't what's meant by Fartlek! It's actually when you combine 'continuous training' with 'interval training'.

Eve's first Fartlek session was a typical one:

Warm-up: easy running for five to ten minutes.
Steady, hard speed for 1.5 to 2.5 kilometres.
Recovery: rapid walking for about five minutes.
Start of speed work: easy running interspersed with sprints of about fifty to sixty metres.
This is repeated until you're a little tired.
Easy running with three or four 'quick steps' now and then (simulating suddenly speeding up to avoid being

overtaken by another runner).
Run full speed uphill for one hundred and seventy-five to
two hundred metres.
Fast pace for one minute.

The whole routine is then repeated until the total time prescribed on the training schedule has elapsed. For Eve, this first session was one hour and fifteen minutes, in order to take the Pensarn to Llandudno 16 route into account. The total session time was actually one hour and thirty minutes, as it's essential that a good warm-up at the start and a cool-down at the end are always included. These will improve performance, minimise post-workout muscle soreness and decrease the chances of being injured.

Each moment spent at Ysgol Abaty or Pen-y-Bryn Hostel was likely to produce an interesting story to tell to your grandchildren. This week was no different and although preparations for the Pensarn to Llandudno 16 were my main distraction, simple tasks like preparing paper for lessons stand out in my memory as well.

At the start of the week, I was pleased to see the arrival of a new stock of paper – two A1 reams, in fact. The students at Ysgol Abaty were able to get through paper like no others I'd ever taught, and the few scraps that remained from the previous year had gone within the first week. Not ideal when one of the lessons you're teaching is Design and Technology.

As I was spending much of my non-teaching time

bonding with the students as they came in and out of the workshop, or working on Eve's race preparation, I hadn't got round to unpacking the newly delivered paper. I seized the chance of getting Michael's help when he came for a visit during one of these non-teaching periods. I'd now learned that whenever a student turned up unannounced, it was best to occupy them productively and find out the reason for the visit later.

Having entered the workshop quietly, Michael was apparently occupying himself with studying the design posters on the wall.

'You OK there, Michael?' I enquired as I carried on brushing the sawdust off one of the benches.

'No problems, Tom, just thought I'd see what yous were doing.'

'Just the usual... cleaning up after one class, before another one comes and messes it all up again,' I joked.

As Michael was a gifted artist and extremely intelligent, I thought he'd be the ideal person to help me quickly convert the A1 sheets into A4 ones.

As I lifted the heavy paper trimmer from under one of the benches onto a cleared table top, I explained, 'I have to cut all this paper down before next week, which is a pain as there's no sizes marked on this trimmer.'

'How'd you do that then, Tom?' Michael politely asked.

'Well, because there's no sizes marked, the easiest thing is to fold the paper in half and cut it. Then you have A2 size. Do that again, and you get A4 pieces... Would you like to give me a hand?' I asked cautiously.

'No worries, Tom, you get on with your jobs, I'm sorted,' Michael assured me as he neatly put one of the reams of paper alongside the paper trimmer.

I left Michael to the task and carried on cleaning away the debris and dust from the previous lesson and proceeded to prepare for *Newton's* arrival.

Despite the ear defenders I was wearing to protect my ears from the high-pitched buzzing of the bandsaw I was using to prepare wood sections for *Newton,* I heard a crash behind me which reverberated around the workshop.

Turning around with an automatic, 'What happened? You OK?'

I could see Michael, his fingers buried deep into his mop of black hair, but no evidence of the paper trimmer or ream of paper.

'Fucking thing!' he shouted as be brought both fists down on the table where the paper trimmer had been stationed.

Having never seen Michael distressed before, I paused momentarily before making the decision to approach him. I was also aware that this might not be the first incident of the day he was involved in, hence his unscheduled arrival at the workshop.

Reassuringly, I pointed out, 'Whatever it is Michael, it's OK. In thirty-seven years from now, no one will even care or remember it – not even you!'

Michael looked at me in puzzlement, not really sure which part of my reassurance applied most. I've always found that distraction is a great tool to use in order to defuse a situation, and thankfully this one works nearly every time.

Turning my attention to the paper trimmer, which I'd now spotted on the floor beside Michael, and the paper scattered around it like blocks of wood at the conclusion of a game of Jenga, I realised what had caused Michael's frustration. Instead of taking a single sheet of paper, and using this as a template to size up the others, Michael had been trying to fold the whole ream, about five hundred sheets, in half, in one action. With enough said, in my opinion, about his outburst, I started to gather up the sheets of paper from the floor. Within a minute, and without being prompted, Michael joined me in the task and, working together, we had the paper trimmer back in place and the paper in a reasonable stack once again.

With the disarray cleared and no condemnation uttered by myself, Michael calmly said, 'Sozz, Tom, I just loose it at times. Do you want me to do something else for yur?'

'You know, what I really need now is a cup of coffee... What about you? You couldn't go to the Cookery Room and ask Alice to make one for the two of us, could you?'

It had become a tactic of mine and Alice's to send any students who needed time out from our lessons to the other person's class on an errand, especially when students were in a 'kicking off' mood. So far, this tactic had proved successful for both of us. By the time Michael and I had finished our coffees, he was his usual placid self again and he went off happily, knowing that he'd got me the coffee I really needed!

This paper-cutting task is one of the best examples

I've ever seen of the difference between intelligence and common sense. It was also an example of how simple instructions aren't so simple after all, especially when students with Autism, as well as EBD, are on the school roll.

Chapter Five
Pensarn to Llandudno 16

With Eve's racing success being the popular topic of conversation among the students, Alice and I decided to take advantage of the students' enthusiasm and put together a running team. It also made practical sense. There was very little chance that Little Dave would allow me and Alice to disappear for the whole day with just one student on a regular basis, but with four students it was a far more realistic proposition. We chose two boys and two girls: Eve, Priya, Martin and Peter.

Selecting the team had been a relatively easy process, with Eve being an obvious first choice. Priya spent all the time she could in Eve's company and, fortunately, even before my arrival at Ysgol Abaty, she'd gone out on some short, slower runs with her friend, so she was the natural second choice. I'd also taken into account Priya's light frame and apparently good cardiovascular system, which was an excellent bonus.

Deciding on which boys to take involved several

conversations between me and Alice. Eve's popularity and success in her first race had worked its magic on the other students. So, we had several boys suddenly interested in running! Even Colin, much to everyone's surprise, was attending our meetings; he managed to sit quietly through them and seemed to take in everything that was discussed. But, in the end, it was Martin and Peter who were brave enough to volunteer to take part in a competition outside the school's safe environment.

Though almost identical in running ability, Martin and Peter were completely different in build and character. Martin, to the untrained eye, didn't look fit at all. He was of average build, with neatly cut dark hair and always wore his black-framed glasses. In reality, he was a natural sportsman with a high ability in football and basketball. Peter, by comparison, would have looked completely at home in the Under-20 Welsh Rugby Squad due to his five foot eleven inches of height, and evenly distributed sixteen stone of weight. Also, although his sixteenth birthday wasn't until the following January, he'd needed to shave for over a year now and, in line with the current fashion, he sported a neat ginger beard complementing his ginger hair.

Once selected, the boys were keen to develop their running ability. For me, when it came to their training, the sense of competition that was apparent between them was a real bonus, as they would go on runs together whenever there was an opportunity on top of following my schedule. Priya, on the other hand, tended to be far more methodical, wanting to follow a detailed training plan to the letter, which I organised for her. So, Alice and I now had four runners, instead of one to train and nurture.

We agreed to set off at 8:30am as the registration desk opened at 9:00am. This allowed plenty of time to settle any nerves before the start of the race at 10am. As the six of us left Pen-y-Bryn and walked out onto the car park, set among the rolling hills above Holywell, our breath was sending smoke signals into the cold morning air.

That's a warning to the others that Ysgol Abaty students are on their way, I thought.

The loud squawking of the resident seagulls greeted us as we drove on the cobbled road over the railway bridge at Pensarn. Luckily, we managed to find a parking space alongside the sea-defence wall.

As we parked up, the four students seemed to ask in unison, 'Where's the toilets?' So, after a quick toilet stop, we made our way to the registration desk at the far end of the car park. The scene around us was full of colour and activity, as race competitors dashed from one place to another. There were far more competitors and spectators than I'd imagined there would be. Alice and I were worried we might lose each other in the crowd, let alone the students for whom we held responsibility.

A photographer from the Rhyl Journal was organising the zone around the start line, trying to capture the most interesting pictures. He was keen to get six young female students from Bangor College under the start banner. They were in matching red crop tops and shorts. Each had a white letter on the front of their top, which spelt out 'BANGOR' when they were in the right order. On their backs, five of the girls had another letter, with the sixth having a large heart. This time, when in the right order, '♥BABES' was displayed. I remembered with fondness having the same easy-going attitude as a first-year student at college in Bangor, enjoying all that life could offer. Even the way they walked to the start line, laughing as they went, was full of excitement and without a care in the world.

How wonderful to enter an event like this, simply for the joy of it, I reflected.

The Pensarn to Llandudno 16 course is unusual in the sporting calendar as it's linear. Most courses – even at cross-country events – have the finish line near, or fairly close to, the start line. I've only taken part in two linear races myself; the first one was my introduction to running – a half marathon from Holywell to Rhyl. Luckily, I was over the moon with my time as a fourteen year old – a few seconds over two hours – otherwise I might not have kept on running. The second was many years later, when I took part in the 1996 Ultimate Mountain Marathon[5] for the third time, which was set in the area around Ardgour in Scotland. On arrival at the start, we were put on coaches and discovered that the real start was actually over an hour and a half away by road. My running partner and I were delighted to be the thirty-fifth fastest male team. Unfortunately, my pleasure was greatly reduced when I discovered that my wife Anne and her partner Lucy were the eleventh fastest female team!

The length of the Pensarn to Llandudno 16 was literally sixteen kilometres. An extra consideration for me and Alice to take into account was where we were going to watch and support the team from; this is always going to be tricky on a straight-line course. Using the North Wales Expressway as a link, Alice and I decided on three spots: the start of the course (as we were already there), towards the halfway point (which we calculated was going to be near Colwyn Bay pier), and then as close to the finishing line as possible – allowing for the crowds that would be gathered there.

Eve made her way to the front in her own unassuming but determined way, somehow pushing in without anyone noticing her. Peter, on the other hand, used his physical presence to get to the fourth or fifth row of runners. As he did so, he acted as a 'defence' for Martin in the same way that a linebacker does for the quarterback in American football. Even so, a wall of competitors was separating the two of them by a metre or so just before the start. Priya, not having the self-confidence or physical presence of the others, was quickly lost from our view, somewhere in the midst of the throng of runners who now engulfed her.

From a road runner's perspective, the course was excellent. There was even tarmac all the way, and only a few short hills to slow you down. You'd be in your stride by the time you tackled the first hill at Llanddulas. The second one, at Penrhyn Bay, would lead you upwards to view the finish line at Llandudno. Once off the cycle track and onto the promenade, there are several benches, as well as cafés, to keep spectators and family members happy as they wait to shout encouragement to the competitors as they run past. The children's paddling pool on the promenade is the marker for your sprint finish. If you have a sprint finish left in you!

We arrived at Colwyn Bay pier just after a group of five runners had passed by. The next collection of runners included Martin, who we cheered on loudly with 'Well done!' and 'Keep going!'

His quick response through snatched, short breaths was, 'It's hard!'

After five minutes or so, and with no sign of Eve, Priya or Peter, we decided to make our way to the finish line. Even so, the busy traffic and some road diversions, due to the staging of the race, meant that we'd struggle to get there in time.

Just as we reached the paddling pool, a car pulled out suddenly in front of us from the roadside, no doubt frustrated by the length of time he'd had to wait because of the increased volume of traffic. A reflex foot on the brake of the minibus, much to the surprise and annoyance of the driver behind us, and a quick turn of the steering wheel meant that we were parked up about twenty-five metres short of the finishing line, just as the front runners were coming into sight behind us. Surprisingly, we were in the right place at the right time.

The first runner, Peter Varley, a teacher from Jersey, crossed in front of us a good five metres ahead of the second runner, who again had another five metres on the third-placed man. We spotted the first female runner just as Peter Varley broke the male finishing tape.

The smile on my face, and the beam on Alice's, displayed our delight; it was Eve! She was in the following pack of five runners all jostling for the ideal position to gain fourth place. Much to my amazement, 'AB', as I thought of her (one of the '♥BABES' from Bangor, who had 'A' on her front and 'B' on her back), was just behind Eve.

Eve then applied her pre-determined tactic. With about twenty-five metres to go, she made her move towards the front. Increasing her stride and pace, it was 'poetry in motion'; everything was perfect. As I grabbed Alice and wondered how we'd celebrate, I froze in my stance. 'AB' had made her move just after Eve, and she was already level with Eve. Before I could even speak to Alice, 'AB' was ahead of Eve and leaving her trailing behind. AB had obviously not just entered the race for the joy of taking part.

Instinctively, I cheered on 'AB' as she broke the women's tape, not just because it was the right thing to do but because she was a class runner. My applause continued, without pause, as Eve came through the finish line a second or two behind her. Eve's time of one hour and five minutes was more than we could have wished for. This was no doubt helped by 'AB' or, to use her correct name, Ann Roberts. Ann came from Abersoch, a small resort on the Llŷn Peninsula which is known for its high property prices. Now it would be known for its high-flying female runner too.

Martin was the next of our team to finish, in a decent

time of one hour and twenty-three minutes. Surprisingly, Priya was the third team member to cross the finish line, in a respectable one hour and thirty-nine minutes, well inside her target of being under one hour and forty-five minutes. Peter had decided to keep pace with a group of runners near the front, doing well until he stopped and knelt on one leg to tighten a lace, close to the fourteen kilometre marker. As soon as he stood up again, the curse of all athletes took hold: cramp! This is sometimes known as 'idiopathic cramp', the cause of which is often unknown. He'd literally limped for the last two kilometres, cheering on Martin and Priya as they passed him – a great credit to his character.

All of us had had a great day out. Eve, Priya, Martin and Peter had all completed the course and now had a recorded race time. Peter was the only one who had a look of disappointment on his face. A born competitor, he'd done so well, but he'd made the mistake of trying to keep up with more experienced runners, without having put in enough training. He was naturally disappointed with his time, but the good news was that he was determined to do better next time, and to take his training more seriously.

As we drove back along the A55 expressway, we were able to look over the race route, now empty of competitors, with just a few walkers or cyclists enjoying the coastal path. By comparison, the wind turbines dominating the horizon far out to sea now seemed full of movement. Alice and I made the spontaneous decision to treat everyone to a snack. The students would have

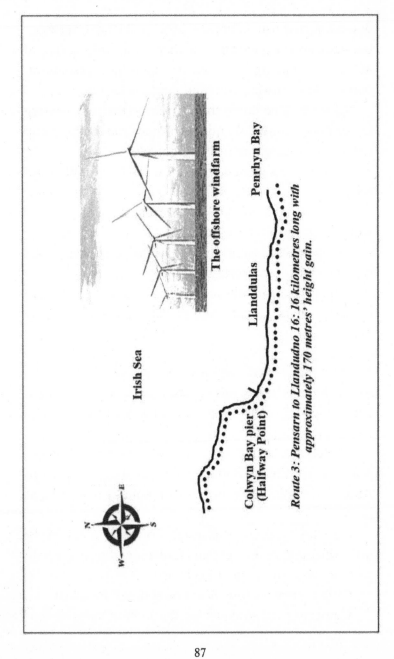

The offshore windfarm

Irish Sea

Llanddulas

Penrhyn Bay

Colwyn Bay pier
(Halfway Point)

Route 3: Pensarn to Llandudno 16: 16 kilometres long with approximately 170 metres' height gain.

opted for their usual choice – McDonald's at Caerwys – but Alice and I decided to treat them to something special as a celebration and opted for the Edenshine Restaurant, part of the Afonwen Craft and Antique Centre.

As we walked down the corridor to the café, passing the display cabinets of antiques, Alice brought the group to a pause to give them all a reminder.

'We've had a great day so far, so let's not spoil things now.'

The four students looked at each other as if butter wouldn't melt in their mouths.

'It's posh here isn't it, so we've got to behave, don't we?' Peter said, reassuringly.

I'm pleased and relieved to report that they reacted to this new environment well, displaying their very best manners.

Later that same week, as I was chatting with Little Dave, Martin and Peter over our hot chocolates, which was now becoming a routine event, Christmas came into our conversation for the first time.

'What are you doing over the winter holidays?' Martin asked me, no doubt a phrase he'd picked up from American films. 'Are you going on holiday or staying at home?'

'I'm staying at home as usual. Christmas is one of my favourite times of the year and I love spending it at home with my wife and girls,' I explained.

'Will you be visiting us at hostel then?' he asked.

I quickly tried to cover up the look of surprise that

Little Dave pointed out was showing on my face. This was one of the many sad moments I experienced at Pen-y-Bryn. I suddenly realised that many of the young people in the hostel wouldn't be going home for Christmas. The simple reason for this being that their families didn't want them.

Now painfully aware of some 'dramatic' episodes that had occurred at Ysgol Abaty since my arrival at the school three months earlier, I fully acknowledged why this might be. Some of the long-term members of staff had told me stories that even now made me cringe with horror. I understood that the potential for a disastrous incident to take place was high. Extended family members, as well as close friends, might be present, which would make matters even more combustible. However, even when I took into account the possibility of vulnerable siblings being present, it didn't seem right that some parents would deliberately decide not to see their sons or daughters at Christmas.

Surprisingly, Eve was one of the many youngsters who didn't go home over the Christmas holiday. When she'd first arrived at Ysgol Abaty, as a fourteen year old, she went home most weekends. This was an easy process compared with some of the other students as she only lived in Wem in Shropshire, which isn't too far away and is even accessible by train from Flint. But, from the age of about sixteen, she'd decided to stay more and more at Pen-y-Bryn Hostel, considering it to be her true home. This was, in great measure, a compliment to the staff who'd spent time building up a positive relationship with her. There was a sense of mutual trust, and Eve enjoyed taking responsibility for her own actions. Within reason, her free time was spent as she pleased.

Enid, one of the LSAs with *Newton*, was also Eve's key worker.

'How do you get on with Eve then? She's well behaved for me in lessons and a super runner,' I asked Enid one day.

'Eve's one of the most independent young people I know. Ever since she first arrived at Pen-y-Bryn, she's been great... Certainly not like some of the ones we get here,' she affirmed.

Apparently, Eve was able to attend a high school, with the help of a support worker, within six weeks of her arrival at Ysgol Abaty. Without fail, she took it upon herself to wash her high school blouse every night in the sink in her room, and then she'd put it on the radiator overnight, meaning that it would be clean and ready to be ironed the next day. I wonder just how many other fourteen year olds, male or female, even think of putting their used clothes in the laundry basket, let alone washing and ironing them.

It might surprise some to learn that Eve washed her own clothes in the sink in her room, rather than using a hostel washing machine. But the alternative was, in fact, a mass wash with clothes belonging to many others at the hostel – some of whom had some extremely unpleasant and unhygienic practices! In Eve's place, I would have done exactly the same thing.

*

As the number of working days until the Christmas holidays became fewer, the excitement of the last school day became greater. On any school day at Ysgol Abaty, it was unlikely that the day would go as planned and often it would call for spur-of-the-moment decisions to be made. Experience had taught the staff members to keep their plans to a minimum – to go with the flow, so to speak. But to create a carefree environment on the very last day, it was agreed that fancy dress would be the dress code for both staff and students. I was told that even some of the most antisocial students would wear a tracksuit, just to be part of the occasion – a great achievement in itself for some of our students.

When the day arrived, I was surrounded by some of the superheroes I'd first met in The Market Cross in Holywell, as well as other well-known characters and celebrities, and it felt like a surreal occasion. Alice and some of the students always provided extra goodies to go with the Christmas dinner that was served up in Pen-y-Bryn Hostel. Games were the order of the day, held at regular intervals, with prizes for everyone. The highlight of the day, for me, was supervising the charades competition, when Colin tried his best to take part without speaking.

In my best teacher's voice, I said, 'You do know the rules now, don't you, Colin?'

'Course, Tom. Please, Tom, it must be my turn now, Tom.'

Colin continued to block my view of the rest of the group as he flitted around in front of me like an annoying housefly that wouldn't go away.

'No one else gives him a go, Tom, cos he always messes it up,' Priya advised, as she indicated 'no' by shaking her head.

'Please, please, Tom. I won't mess it up, Tom, honest, Tom.'

'No talking, Colin, OK?' I reinforced.

'OK, Tom, no talking. I promise...'

So, with apprehension, I gave Colin what I thought was one of the easier cards which I'd prepared the night before. On it was written: Television: *Match Of The Day*.

'Television,' Colin said as he outlined a square with his hands.

This immediately brought a bombardment of adverse comments from the students.

'Told you, Tom.'

'He always does this.'

'He can't play properly, Tom.'

I beckoned Colin over to me and put my hands gently on his shoulders to try and ensure I had his full attention.

'Colin, you're not allowed to talk,' I said again.

Colin nodded his head in agreement as he held both hands up in a thumbs-up position. Repeating the mime for the television, he then started striking his chest in an upward movement with his right hand as if he was frantically trying to force closed a jammed zip on his jumper. This created many inspired guesses from Colin's audience, such as *Tarzan* and *Hitchhiker's Guide to the Galaxy*, but there was one guess that I quickly had to censor.

'The divvy's practising wanking again, Tom,' was hurled across the classroom, courtesy of a giggling Roy.

Fortunately, at least in Roy's case, a stern look and the simple statement, 'Remember... Everton's on the television tonight,' was enough. I knew he wouldn't do anything to jeopardise his chances of being able to watch the match.

Colin's ongoing miming included running from one end of the room to the other and jumping up and down as he turned around. This, especially when he fell over doing so, brought fits of laughter from everyone present. Words really did seem to come out of his mouth without any control on his part.

'It... when... you know,' were frequently used, often followed by, 'Sozz, Tom.'

After a few minutes, and without warning, Colin shouted out, 'Match of the Day!' Then, with a broad smile on his face, he added, 'I've won, Tom.'

Priya, as she moved into a more comfortable sitting position, justified her earlier remarks. 'Didn't I tell you, Tom?'

At the end of the competition, I signalled to Colin to come over to me with a friendly gesture and simply asked, 'What were you doing hitting your chest?'

'Lighting me match, wasn't I, Tom.'

It was common practice for the students who smoked to use the zip on their jackets, coats or even jeans as a striking surface. Now his mime made complete sense.

Although not initially desired by the students, Colin's mime provided the loudest laughs of the day for staff and students alike.

As I set off home at 5:02pm, I was completely exhausted. I'd had a wonderful day and the best thing of all was that there hadn't been a single entry made in the incident log.

I decided not to spend any time at Pen-y-Bryn during my Christmas holidays. Even with Ysgol Abaty's shorter terms and regular breaks, when any holiday week arrived, it was needed more than at any other time in my teaching career. As well as giving me the opportunity to spend some time with my family and friends, this holiday also included Boxing Day which, for many living in my home area, meant 'Roll the Barrel' in Denbigh. Starting back in 1958, to raise funds for local charities, it now attracted hundreds of spectators, as well as competitors, from all over the world.

The day's proceedings usually start when the Flint and Denbigh Hunt arrives, filling the town's high street with colour and noise. Hounds seem to be running everywhere, loving the attention they receive from the spectators who try to find viewing points among the hay bales which border the barrel course. Once the stirrup cup has been presented, the hunt sets off on its way around the Vale. Any not-so-pleasant reminders that the horses and dogs have been in the area are removed and, with a central line of bales added, the course is complete.

When I'd attended my first Boxing Day at Denbigh with my wife in 1985, it wasn't the Roll the Barrel competition or the hunt that had attracted me. As attractive as these undoubtedly were, the biggest draw was the pubs! Because of local market-town licensing laws, the pubs in Denbigh were open all day. This may seem like a usual occurrence now, but when I was young, pubs in Wales had strict opening and closing times. With hindsight, the fact that no pubs were open on a Sunday in Bangor, where I attended college, probably helped to reduce the number of alcoholics among the Welsh teaching profession. There were several pubs in the area that had lock-ins, where alcohol would be served to a select few out of licensing hours, but in Denbigh on Boxing Day, you could drink all day long. It was a day to meet up with friends and family who you might not see for the rest of the year. The pubs were cleared of furniture and fittings, sawdust was laid on the floors, and drinking a pint of ale in every pub was the target for everyone. All the pubs, many now sadly closed, would be full to bursting with drinkers enjoying the occasion. Even the streets would be crowded with people making their way around the town, attempting the challenge of visiting every pub before fatigue or the consequences of the alcohol took effect.

You might think that rolling a barrel between some hay bales sounds like a fun activity, and you'd be right. All are encouraged to take part and recently a junior course has been set up in the square, just off the high street. But if you're thinking you might have a go and possibly win, think again. Firstly, unless you're practised in the skill of rolling a barrel, you'll quickly discover that they have a mind of their own. They'll set off, with the slightest touch, rolling in all directions apart from the one you want. Secondly, there are a few local families, usually of farming stock, who've set up their own courses at home. Practising throughout the year, and passing techniques on from one generation to the next, the same limited number of surnames will appear in the local press as winners year after year. I was tempted, when I first saw the competition, to take part, but my better judgement prevented me from doing so. Many of my friends have participated, usually with little success.

On this occasion, as I looked across the high street to the other side, I could see Little Dave and Martin sheltering from the rain under the overhangs of the Tudor buildings. Requests for competitors were heard repeatedly over the PA system as the rain got heavier. In the spirit of good competition, gloves would be passed to novices who weren't yet aware of the dangers involved. Supportive cheering would encourage all to finish their heat, before the finals could take place. After an hour of enthusiastic competition, you could watch the women's and men's winning cups being awarded, before, more quickly than you might imagine, the high street was back to its normal state. The only evidence that the morning's events had taken place would be a few stalks of straw trapped in corners, undetected by the team of volunteers as they carried out their cleaning duties.

I managed to speak to Little Dave and Martin before they set off for their dinner at Pen-y-Bryn. Martin, who hadn't set foot out of London before arriving at Pen-y-Bryn Hostel, situated on the moors between the villages of Brynford and Pantasaph, hadn't seen anything like the Boxing Day events at Denbigh before. He'd taken it all in, asking if I'd seen all the dogs running around. He'd noted the diverse hunt members – old and young, with appropriately sized horses, all in their bright hunt jackets. The Roll the Barrel competition had been the icing on the cake for him. As Little Dave guided him away from the high street, down the narrow lane to the car park, he was still enthusing about the competition.

Martin was full of ideas of how we could set up a course at the hostel and practise throughout the year by getting old barrels from the Crooked Horn pub in Brynford. He imagined that the winners next time would be staff or students from Pen-y-Bryn.

As I was waving them off from the car park, Martin wound down his window and, with a broad smile on his face, shouted:

'Tom, we could have "Roll the Barrel" on sports day!'

Chapter Six
A Fresh Fall of Snow

The first Tuesday of January arrived and as I was parking the car outside Ysgol Abaty, in my usual slot of course, I thought back to my first sighting of an Ysgol Abaty student: Colin. He'd appeared out of the Art Room window and then, just as quickly, disappeared over the rooftops.

It's strange, I concluded, *a similar action now would hardly be worth noting*.

I felt an unusual mix of emotions as I got out of the car. The nature of the job demanded a dependence on the team around you and consequently a strong bond built up among the staff. In a similar way, you had to establish a positive relationship with the students to be able to carry out any successful teaching. Although many teachers wouldn't care to admit it, at some of the larger high schools, there are teachers who can't recognise some of their students beyond the school setting, even after a term's lessons. Compare this with Ysgol Abaty where, after only one lesson, their image is stored in your memory banks forever. You can appreciate the emotional difference. The essentially strong connection between staff and students meant that despite all the challenges Ysgol Abaty held, I actually looked forward to going back to work.

As usual, I was the first member of the teaching staff to arrive at school and noted that the clock said 7:31am as I entered the staffroom. A minute off my preferred time, but I'd learned from experience that I could lose minutes easily if Susan was at her hatch and we had our usual morning chat. I flicked the isolating switch down and put the hot water geyser on. A combination of economics and health and safety meant that it had been turned off for the festive period. The old system of 'first in, put the kettle on' was about as useful as an iron in a nudist camp... Then again, an iron does remove creases!

Not only teachers, but everyone who shares a staffroom will know the frustration of missing out on a hot drink because there's not enough 'kettle time'. With the kettle often only coming to the boil at the end of your break, you'll have only enough time for a few sips before the remainder is poured into the sink and you return to your workplace.

The geyser, when it was installed in the middle of the autumn term, was 'warmly' appreciated by all. Its instant supply of boiling water had a magical effect on staff morale. It did require the addition of a large sign above it after the first week though, as Simon had tried to reach around Little Dave to top up his morning coffee during the briefing and had caused an injury. To get around anyone in the small kitchen area would have been difficult; to get around Little Dave would have been almost impossible. The resulting splash of boiling water onto Little Dave's arm as he was washing up, produced a surprising lack of obscenities. The severe scalding, evident the next day, resulted in the large sign, '*DŴR BERWEDIG* – BOILING WATER', which now dominated the space above the geyser.

By 9:17am, it was as if I'd never been on holiday. Some quick hellos to staff members interrupted my set pattern of morning tasks until the wagon train of minibuses and taxis started to arrive. Only when all the staff are fully prepared are the students allowed out of their taxis. When the signal is given, the waves of students flow through the entrance door like revellers on a Saturday night when a nightclub door is first opened.

Dan, who made up for his diminutive stature with plenty of noise, set the tempo of the day by climbing out of the side window of the first minibus that entered the school car park shouting 'Fuck, fuck, fuck!' at the top of his voice.

He then set off across the playing field, away from the main school entrance. Helen, who a moment earlier had been standing next to me, was in close pursuit. Thankfully, I was due to teach *Wordsworth* later in the day, which was lucky as I was sure Helen wouldn't be back in time to support *Wordsworth* during their first lesson.

Bethan, the youngest in *Wordsworth*, who was always

willing to compete for attention, saw Dan's actions as an excuse for her to be part of the commotion. A moment earlier she'd been calmly walking with Priya from her taxi to the school entrance. Now her catchphrase, 'I don't know what their fucking problem is,' in her broad Wolverhampton accent, was echoing around the Greenfield Valley and into the valleys beyond.

Bethan's parents were well-mannered and Welsh speaking. They'd moved to Merry Hill, a suburb of Wolverhampton, a year before Bethan was born, so consequently Bethan's dialect was pure 'Black Country'. The contrast of accents when I sat in on her reviews always amused me – as did how such a petite thirteen-year-old girl could come out with such coarse phrases. The volume of caterwauling she managed to achieve is still a wonder to me, and she was always trying to move up the pecking order within the school. Even though she was young, she'd been put in *Wordsworth* among the older girls in the hope that their maturity might rub off on her. I'd initially come across her during my first lesson with *Wordsworth* when I'd realised that she was the one who'd headbutted the wall. More notably, I would soon come across her again on my break time duty when she and Colin would decide to run amok. Yet for reasons some staff members couldn't understand, I'd developed a soft spot for her.

On the break time occasion, the school-controlled clock hadn't reached eleven, the official start of the morning break, and already chaos prevailed. Colin didn't want to be left out and, considering himself to be fearless, he'd put his fist through one of the large window panes in the old part of the school.

I found out later that on one of his various escape attempts from the staff, he'd run around an outside corner of the building and stumbled into Alan.

'This bairn's being a propa worky ticket; if he's not careful there'll be no kets toneet,' was Alan's response as he literally lifted Colin off his feet.

Colin had had no choice but to dangle there while Alan chastised him in front of several of the other students. Despite not fully understanding what Alan was saying, and being wild with anger, Colin knew better than to confront him. So, unable to accept the superiority Alan had demonstrated, Colin had vented his anger on the large window pane in the outer wall of the History classroom.

As much of the school had been an old country house, many of the windows were tall sash ones with large panes. Any student who broke one would gain great kudos from most of the others and so consequently, they were smashed on a regular basis, with spectacular displays of broken fragments spraying in all directions.

Each time a pane of glass was broken, Bryn, our maintenance man, had the task of repairing it as quickly as possible by adding clear Fablon on top of the new pane. This was a cheap alternative to toughened or safety glass, considered a good idea by the Ysgol Abaty management. The students, however, seemed to have a sixth sense, which made them 'kick off' near the old unprotected panes on nearly every occasion.

Despite our best intentions, using Fablon as a safety measure had had the knock-on effect of providing large pieces of glass for the students to 'play with' once the pane had been smashed. Colin was now smiling broadly, glass all around him, admiring his handiwork. But Bethan, as she often did, apparently to impress Colin, stole the show. Taking hold of one of the larger pieces of triangular glass, she announced:

'You think that's bosting; watch this then.'

She then plunged the sharpest point of glass into her left arm midway between her wrist and elbow. Blood poured all around as Bethan waved her arm about, showing off her achievement. Colin, wisely, decided not to argue the point any further; after all, Bethan was still holding the glass. As I witnessed this, a shiver went down my spine. I found it hard to accept Bethan's total disregard for her own well-being. As one of the registered First Aiders, the rest of my break was taken up by assisting Bethan with a mixture of first aid and counselling.

Sitting Bethan down, it was difficult trying to stop her from waving her arm around so that she could show off her injury to the other students who hovered nearby for a closer look. Also, of course, it was difficult to try and avoid Bethan's blood going all over me.

'Oh, Bethan, what have you done to yourself now?' I said.

Bethan looked intently at her arm.

'It's bosting isn't it, Tom?' she said and began flapping her arm around and sprinkling blood everywhere.

'No, Bethan... listen to me, it's not good at all!'

'Look at them all trying to look at me now, Tom. They want to see the blood, don't they?'

Luckily, as Bethan was saying this, the last of the interested students were being ushered away into the school by the other staff who were on duty.

'Bethan, no one can see you now, so please sit still and let me sort this... please. Hopefully it's not too deep.'

'OK... they're gone now, Tom, so it don't matter anymore.'

I carefully put a padded dressing over the cut and applied as much pressure as I could with a bandage as I could see that the outer part of the dressing already had blood seeping through it. Thankfully with no students now in sight, Bethan was at least sitting in a more relaxed manner.

'Thank you. Now listen; you don't take this off,' I said. 'You hold your arm up here. Dai Twice will get someone to take you to the hospital, and you'll probably need stitches, OK!'

Bethan stared straight into my eyes and a grin appeared on her face. 'How many stitches do you think I'll get this time, Tom? My record's twenty-six.'

'Bethan, forget about the number of stitches; sit still and keep your arm up. Here comes Enid now, probably to take you to the hospital.'

'Tara-a-bit!' she shouted as she went off with her uninjured arm held securely by Enid.

'Why this time, Bethan?' I heard Enid ask as she made her way with Bethan to one of the minibuses.

At lunchtime, Bethan came running into the workshop with her arm in an elevated sling.

'Only eighteen stitches this time, Tom, so yous were right; it weren't deep.' She beamed, and then she was off again.

After lunchtime, things had settled down. I'd made the decision not to make the trek from the workshop to the staffroom. I was going to reflect, in solitude, on how I'd survived the morning's events. Surely, it wasn't supposed to be this difficult after the Christmas holidays. These musings were similar to the ones you experience on the first days of your annual ski holiday. The first couple of hours on the slopes seem to be a combination of hard work and falling over. Even simple routes involve more thought and energy than you'd remembered. Returning to Ysgol Abaty after a holiday period had exactly the same feeling, except the last thing you'd want there would be snow!

Although the Christmas holidays now felt distant, the first week in December was still very fresh in my memory. It had brought six inches of snow for Brynford and Pantasaph, and even more had accumulated in drifts at the sides of the roads and the edges of the fields. Greenfield itself had none, which shows the difference that just a couple of miles can make when there's considerable height gain. As is often the case, I knew the night before that there would be snow on the ground the next day. I'd realised at a young age that my sense of smell seemed to be overly acute. My mother has repeatedly told me that as a toddler, I'd run up to objects, as well as people, and sniff away at them, causing her endless embarrassment. But one of the benefits was, even when young, I could always predict when snow was about to fall. I've tried to explain my acute awareness of scents to others, but have had little success.

So, as I'd predicted to both my daughters, a good covering of snow could be seen all around as I opened the curtains the following morning. I was amazed, though, at the high walls of ploughed snow around Caerwys as I travelled to work; the snow was higher than the car in many places.

I arrived at Ysgol Abaty to a mixture of calm and frantic activity. More cars were scattered around the car park than usual, though luckily none had taken 'my' parking space. Some of the staff members, who'd set off from home earlier than usual, had found the coast roads clear of snow and were now enjoying a leisurely hot drink in the staffroom. Others were madly talking on the three phones that the office switchboard would allow to be used at any one time. Their task was to warn the Pen-y-Bryn houses and the contracted taxi firms not to try to reach Ysgol Abaty as it was too dangerous to drive on the surrounding roads. Gareth, as head teacher, along with Dai Twice and Simon, as the senior members of hostel staff on duty, had made the decision that, for the rest of the day at least, all students would remain at Pen-y-Bryn Hostel.

Young people today have a reputation for drug and alcohol abuse. Fortunately, Pen-y-Bryn staff usually had few problems with either, and even on the occasions when minimal amounts of drugs or alcohol were brought back after a holiday period, the contraband was quickly confiscated with little fallout from the students afterwards. A fresh fall of snow, however, was far more concerning for all members of staff!

At times like this, all normal rules and standards disappeared, though the main weapon in the staff's arsenal was Simon. I'd learned to respect Simon on many levels – after all, he was the first 'Superman' I'd ever met! Naturally good at all sports, as well as outdoor pursuits, we'd discovered we had a lot in common. He was also a really nice guy. The students loved going on his adventure days, though they weren't popular with all of the staff. But Enid had enthused about Simon's days out ever since she'd learned of my own adventurous nature.

'You'll love Simon's trips; they're wicked,' was how she'd put it.

Unfortunately, our different work patterns had prevented me from experiencing one yet.

You had to be there to really appreciate the effect that the snow had on the students. Many had seen very little, if any, snow before. A cocktail of the excitement that snow brings to all those who are young at heart and the 'over-excitable' nature of many of the children was explosive. But one of the great things about working at Ysgol Abaty was that you never knew what was going to happen next.

An hour after selecting my usual parking spot at Ysgol Abaty, I was reversing into my usual parking spot at

Pen-y-Bryn Hostel. To steal a line from the Christmas carol 'Good King Wenceslas', the snow all around Pen-y-Bryn was *deep and crisp and even*. And as I'd predicted, perhaps even feared, the students were 'high' on the white wilderness that lay before them. I'd made the effort to leave home two hours earlier than usual, to ensure I made it through the snow to get to work on time. But maybe I should have made a phone call excusing myself instead?

Anyone who's grown up in the hills or mountains of North Wales will find it hard to accept the fact that other youngsters may not have experienced the same pleasure of newly fallen snow each winter. As most of the students at Ysgol Abaty had grown up in inner-city areas or further south, they were in 'overload' about what they were seeing through the hostel windows. I tried to remember my childhood excitement at the first fall of snow, and looking around the dining room, where all the students were assembled, I could recall what it was like fully.

Soon Simon was sitting at the front of the dining room, close to the kitchen serving hatch. All of the students, and most of the staff, were mesmerised by what he was saying. Tales of winter climbs in Snowdonia and other parts of the world were brought to life, as he produced specialist items out of his rucksack, having had the foresight to bring props with him from home. As he spoke of Hillary's first ascent of Everest, he produced the same model ice axe with its forged head and wooden handle. Then, with perfect timing, he pulled out the modern, highly colourful equivalent. Helmets, crampons and boots were all passed around the room. Dan was asked to model some of the gear, though his slight stature meant that he was barely able to stand with the weight of Simon's winter pack on his back.

When Enid suddenly announced through the serving hatch, 'Who'd like a hot drink and biscuits?' the students reacted as if she'd interrupted their favourite film at a crucial scene.

I glanced at the clock at the back of the dining room and couldn't believe the time. 11:30am! Simon had kept us fully entertained for one and a half hours. No wonder Enid had such high respect for him – a respect I was now fully starting to appreciate.

With our warm drinks and a few biscuits inside us, we ventured outside into the whiteness where the undulating landscape of Pantasaph seemed more uniform due to the heavy fall of snow. Simon had divided the staff and students into groups and the first task was for the teams to try to take over the monument at the top of Pen-y-Ball. This was to be guarded by the largest team. Needless to say, the students ran around frantically, whooping and screaming, and snowballs were thrown with extreme gusto!

Then, having exhausted the students' initial excitement and energy, a more skilful task was set by Simon. After demonstrating how to build a windbreak out of snow (basically an igloo without a roof), Simon set the groups of students the task of building the largest one possible within a set time. I think Simon knew just how exhausting this would become after the first few blocks were laid – another much-needed drain on the students' energy levels.

The final task of the day was a competition to build the largest snowman. It must have looked like a scene from an alien planet to passing motorists, as they made their commute back home. The landscape surrounding the standing stone was now filled with walled structures guarded by giant white sentinels.

The failing daylight was a signal to bring the day's activities to a close. The trek back to Pen-y-Bryn, although less than one hundred metres, was a slow one, with everyone recalling their favourite moments of the wintry day. None of the students had wanted lunch at the usual time, so a rush towards the dining room ensued. They were sitting in their teams, for the most part, with staff and students seated together without any obvious hierarchy. Having taken off their outer layers, steam now rose from their overworked bodies. There were red, glowing faces all around as they chatted away to each other. Then, with the arrival of their well-earned dinner, the most profound silence of all silences filled the dining room.

After enjoying the meal with my fellow teammates, I set off home with the shadows of our creations just visible in the dying light. As I made my way carefully through the corridors of snow, created by the snowploughs around Caerwys town, I made a point of recording mentally the goodness of the day. I knew it would help to balance out any days that were challenging in the future.

*

The first part of my teaching day had gone well enough to plan. I had even been able to think back to the enjoyment of that snowy winter's day, spent with staff and students, a month earlier. Looking out of the window now, there was no evidence that snow had ever settled here. The last few patches had been washed away by overnight rain a week ago.

As I was brushing the worktops clear of the sawdust that had gathered during my first lessons, and recharging myself ready for *Wordsworth's* arrival, Alice and Eve came into the workshop.

Alice always knew how to brighten up my day. She and Eve were carrying freshly made coffee, including a homemade mocha for me. Eve was full of news of her training over the festive period.

'Hi, Tom, Eve wants to tell you all about her training,' Alice announced as she handed me my coffee.

Looking straight into my eyes, Eve said, 'On Saturday I did my long run – not too many hills, like you said, Tom. Then, on Sunday, I had my breakfast and only ran five kilometres because you said I had to have short runs. When I got up on Monday, it was raining so I didn't run till the afternoon. I decided to run down to school and back. There were no staff there, so I didn't go in.'

'There wouldn't be—' I tried to break her flow, but was cut short.

'There's more, Tom,' said Alice, raising her eyebrows.

'I had a great run on Tuesday,' Eve continued without seeming to draw breath, 'Don't know how far, but I kept going for three hours and four minutes, passed some other runners who were going really slow! Wednesday, I...'

The diary of training continued – in great detail. I sat back in my chair, sipped my coffee and accepted the inevitable.

I soon realised that Alice had actually been quite strategic, as she'd brought Eve in to see me to give her own ears a rest! Nevertheless, hearing Eve's tales of her training regime and activities over the previous three weeks was a breath of fresh air and set me up perfectly for the arrival of the other girls in *Wordsworth*.

Eve, as I'd expected, had followed her training schedule to the letter. She'd even taken care not to overindulge in the vast amount of food and drink that filled up Pen-y-Bryn during the Christmas period.

As it was my usual Tuesday shift that evening, I had plenty of time to clear away the debris from the day's lessons, and even sorted out some of the junk I'd inherited when I took over from the previous teacher.

How time flies when you're enjoying yourself, I thought.

Mr Morgan, my predecessor, was a giant of a man. In the staffroom, there's a photograph of Alice with Mr Morgan and Little Dave standing on either side of her. Alice looks like a little girl between them; the top of her head only just reaching their chests. Everyone seemed to like him; even the students spoke well of him. Then, at the end of one school day, he'd gone into Gareth Lee's office and calmly handed him two envelopes, formally marked with 'Mr Gareth Lee, Head Teacher'. The first contained his notice. The second a doctor's note, giving stress as his reason for leaving.

Apparently, the only thing he said to Gareth was, 'Please thank everyone for their help and support, but I can't work here any longer.' Then after a quick shake of Gareth's hand, he turned and left. He never returned to Ysgol Abaty.

It was while I was having dinner – chilli and rice – with a few of the lads from *Shakespeare* that Martin came over.

'Little Dave is asking if he can please have a word with you, Tom?' he said.

All the students and staff called David Littler, 'Little Dave'. He truly reminded me of Little John, in *Robin Hood*, his title and physique being a complete mismatch.

What have I done wrong? I wondered.

It's strange how most people react this way to authority. For me, it was an instinctive reaction because, as a boy, I'd spent many of my own school lessons with teachers who'd wanted to 'have a word with me'!

Fortunately, Little Dave quickly got to the point before I had a chance to start my list of excuses for errors I might have made.

'I keep hearing good things about you from the staff, and the students all seem to like you too.'

I immediately relaxed my defensive stance.

'How do you fancy working in the hostel on a Saturday or Sunday every other week for ten hours instead of the five hours every Tuesday?' he asked as he signalled me to sit down.

'Well, it's nice to know people think I'm doing well. But I'll have to talk to my wife Anne before I can let you know about working weekends,' I replied diplomatically, as this gave me thinking time before committing myself to anything.

'Well, let me know,' he added, turning to gather some papers from the top of one of the filing cabinets. 'You can take some of the students off-site for the day and that means I'll have less of them here for my staff to cope with.'

'Thank you, I'll catch up with you next week and let you know,' I said as I walked out the door.

Even before the following Tuesday had arrived, I'd approached Little Dave to take him up on his offer. I was now able to head straight home at 3:45pm, as I was due to work the following Sunday.

Chapter Seven
Working On Sundays

As I made my way straight to Pen-y-Bryn Hostel on my first Sunday, I realised just what a long day I'd set myself up for, but I'd already decided I was going to enjoy it.

After seeking agreement from the hostel staff who were on duty, my plan was to play it safe on this first occasion. My first outing was offered to Eve, Priya, Martin and Peter, partly as a reward for their excellent behaviour at the Pensarn to Llandudno 16, but also because I thought they were a safe option. Needless to say, they all quickly took up the offer.

The activity I'd prepared was a walk over the summit of Moel Siabod. It's the highest mountain in the Moelwynion Range, its summit being at eight hundred and seventy-two metres, and although not one of the famous fifteen peaks that are over three thousand feet high, it's one of my favourites. Also, weather permitting, it gives wonderful views of the rest of Snowdonia, including Snowdon itself. Eve would be able to look down on sections of her first race, undertaken back in November, and retell it to the other students.

Blue sky with a few small, cotton-wool cumulus clouds always indicated that it was going to be good weather for several hours, and the weather forecast for my first Sunday shift at Pen-y-Bryn backed this up. I was full of enthusiasm as I arrived. My brown bread and Cheddar cheese sandwiches were made, my stainless-steel flask was full of coffee and I had the obligatory chocolate bar with me: a Mars bar, of course, to help me '*work, rest and play*'.

I pulled up in my unusually clean Skoda, still shining in the sunlight after its Saturday wash. I noted just how empty the car park was, but even so, I parked in my usual space. I found the same emptiness as I walked through the corridors of Pen-y-Bryn Hostel. I made my way to the dining room where, regardless of the time of day, I could always find at least one person. There, chatting cheerfully, were Helen, Eve, Priya, Martin and Colin.

'Good morning, Tom, am I glad to see you!' Helen called out. She stood up, adding with emphasis, 'It's been a long night!'

'Again?' I replied with a frown on my face as I sat down next to Martin.

Peter, who I'd expected to see with the others, had apparently trashed his room during the previous night. This had followed an argument about which biscuits were available to have with his drink before going to bed. It was one of those 'if only' moments, according to the staff who were around at the time. *If only* the girls choosing the biscuits hadn't picked ginger nuts; *if only* Alan hadn't decided, in his strong Geordie accent, to keep asking Peter, 'Have yous got a couple of ginger nuts, man?'

Peter, as big and muscular as he was, was wise enough not to take on Alan unless there was no other alternative. Which was just as well, as even the best and largest of the hostel staff would have had trouble separating the two of them. The alternative action, which Peter had taken, was to storm out of the dining room, leaving the assembled hostel staff trying to ensure that Alan didn't follow him to continue his ribbing.

'All we could do was wait patiently outside his room and listen to the sound of the stuff inside being broken,' Helen revealed.

From past experience, they knew that Peter wouldn't harm himself. But by the time the room was quiet again, and staff members had ventured inside, there were only a handful of items left undamaged.

Little Dave came into the dining room with his usual air of authority.

As he helped himself to a coffee, he looked at the assembled group and called over to me, 'There's no way Peter can go with you after his antics last night, but I still want you to take four students off-site.'

He was also concerned that Peter's mood might not have improved since the previous evening and, in light of this, he'd need as few of the other students around him as possible.

'Colin's been pretty good lately, so I've decided to

give him a carrot,' was his proposal.

Wanting to keep a good reputation among the hostel staff, I amicably replied, 'That's no problem at all.'

Colin hadn't been involved in any major incidents recently and deserved recognition for this, so I agreed fully with Little Dave's assessment of the situation. But the last thing I wanted, on my first Sunday outing, was to return and have to ask for an incident form. My expectations for the day had suddenly decreased immensely. Colin would always be the 'white ninja' in my mind – the one I saw disappearing over the school roof as I arrived on my first day. He was the student who'd stood out from all the others when I'd had my first meal at Pen-y-Bryn.

Although I'd built up a positive relationship with Colin, especially after we'd been in the same team on the winter adventure day organised by Simon back in December, I was fully aware of how difficult he could be to manage. Not least because he had a great knack of winding up all the other students – which often led to staff members having unnecessary confrontations with other students, who were even more difficult than Colin to manage. I wondered if Little Dave was thinking more about this side of Colin's character than his recent spell of good behaviour when he chose Colin as Peter's replacement. Thinking of what the day ahead could bring, I reminded myself again that I was going to enjoy it.

In most schools, a change in the format of an outing, such as including different students in the excursion, would require the staff to fill in more paperwork – the endless paperwork that always seems to be involved with anything you do in education. Risk assessments, parental or, as in this case, hostel consent forms, and equipment checklists would all have to be redone. Perhaps even pre-visits, in the staff's own time, would have to be completed. However, I was given £30 for expenses and instructed to 'be back about six' by Little Dave as he left the dining room.

Just as we were about to drive off in the minibus, Enid started waving at me as she ran past the front of the minibus. ('Enid' is pronounced the Welsh way. Enid as in 'Enid Blyton' is the more popular pronunciation in England, but Enid is actually a Welsh name, from the word meaning 'life' or 'soul'.)

'Little Dave agreed that I could join you,' she shouted, 'as lots of the kids are at home this weekend. Hope that's OK?'

She jumped into the front passenger seat of the minibus and the probability that I was going to enjoy the day increased greatly.

I'd first noticed Enid at the Market Cross in Holywell on my introductory staff night out, and I'd had my first chance to talk to her properly during my initial week at Ysgol Abaty when she'd turned up as 'supply' for Helen with the students from *Wordsworth*. During the winter term, she'd also managed to get a job as one of the hostel staff. Among other things, this had meant a lot more money for her.

Enid was actually a qualified teacher from Anglesey. However, after just one year of teaching at one of her local high schools, and at just twenty-three, she'd made the decision to ditch the growing mountains of paperwork and actually spend time working with children instead.

All of the staff and students liked her, and it was simple to understand why. Athletic in build, with long dark hair and a friendly demeanour, she usually arrived at work looking more like she was about to enjoy a night on the town than work in a special school. And she seemed even more impressive as she came to work on her motorbike. I'd be the first to admit that my knowledge of motorbikes is limited, to say the least, but even I know that 'Harley Davidson' on the side of the fuel tank means something special. Enid's motorbike of choice was a 1974 Harley XLCH Sportster. Many teenagers have a specialist subject or favourite topic, and they acquire a great wealth of knowledge in it. Fortunately, one of Colin's specialist subjects was motorbikes. In fact, Enid explained, as she sat alongside me, Colin had spent most of the previous evening telling everyone, 'Tom's taking me scrambling.'

What no one realised initially was that he'd mixed up motorbike scrambling with mountain scrambling – that is, making your way over steep and rocky ground, often having to use your hands.

'Scrambling in Snowdonia started my own mountain expertise,' Simon had explained to Colin, 'and Tom will be taking you up a real mountain.' After that, he was just as keen to join me for the day.

By the time I'd turned right onto the A5, I no longer had a limited knowledge of motorbikes. Enid had already 'wowed' Colin, when she came out with, 'I rebuilt the top of my Harley's engine myself.'

Parts like NOS Manley-forged pistons, Mikuni carburettors and Branch inlet manifolds were now all known to me. But my professional description of her bike would still have to be: black with high handlebars and lots of shiny chrome.

By the time we'd parked at a favourite café of mine beside the A5, I appreciated just how easy it was for everyone to like Enid. She chatted to all five of us as if we were great friends, never seeming to miss anyone out. Although humour seemed to be integral to every part of her conversation, her delivery was always professional. I learned that, when at home on her parents' Anglesey farm, she'd handle large animals with ease. Also, that she had a second dan, or black belt, in Shotokan Karate, having represented Wales the previous year. The perfect person to have around if any of the students 'kicked off'! Yes, the day actually had the makings of being a very good one indeed.

Leaving the café after finishing our drinks, I looked at the students' faces staring up at Moel Siabod. I was reminded, once again, that they were just children. For all their banter and false bravado, contemplating their first attempt at the summit of a mountain, even Moel Siabod, was showing in the apprehension on their faces. Safety instructions and guidance had been given during our drive and now, after some words of reassurance from Enid and myself about how great the day was going to be, we set off, crossing the bridge on the other side of the road.

When the weather is favourable, there can be few places more breathlessly exquisite than Snowdonia. The gradual walk up the track did away with any need for warm-up stretches and allowed all of us to leave behind our troubles as we chatted together.

As the path became more uneven, the small quarry pool, smooth and azure in colour, was the perfect place for our 'elevenses'. As we sat enjoying our chocolate bars and sipping from our flasks, I looked again at the quiet and rugged landscape around us. I wondered if I would ever, on a hot summer's day, have that swim in the inviting quarry pool that I've always promised myself on my 'next visit'. Without doubt, I consider Moel Siabod to be the perfect mountain for beginners to experience the pleasure of mountain walking. It truly gives you the feeling of all that a mountain can offer and yet, treated with the right respect, is completely safe. And I didn't envisage the students having any difficulty with the 'grade 1' scramble I'd chosen.

As we approached the scramble, I could see another group of walkers who'd taken one of the more difficult routes on the Daear Ddu face; it could be that they were more experienced than their attire suggested, or perhaps it was their first ascent of Moel Siabod! I knew that my less challenging choice of route would test out any fear of heights that the students had, or unnecessary nerves, as we conquered the first section of bouldering. Then, with Enid at the front and me at the rear, we followed the line of the group ahead, avoiding the trickier section on the right, where the other group had already come to a halt. We turned towards our left and completed the final scramble with ease. Once on the plateau, it was then just a short walk to the summit.

With a smile on my face, I said, 'Good morning' to the group we'd overtaken on the way up, as they arrived twelve minutes after we'd sat down. This was followed by a polite series of 'hellos' from the students, with reciprocal 'hellos' from the group as they continued on their way southwards towards Blaenau Dolwyddelan.

Sitting among the summit rocks, we were able to enjoy our sandwiches while taking in the wonderful panoramic views of Snowdonia, including many of the peaks that are over three thousand feet high. I consider this perspective to be equal in grandeur to the view of the Snowdon massif from the east end of Llynnau Mymbyr, near the Plas y Brenin National Outdoor Centre, though of course that outlook from Llynnau Mymbyr requires a lot less effort to experience!

Once lunch was finished and we were feeling refreshed, we followed the ridge around in a clockwise direction. As it was a clear day, we were able to view the route of our ascent in the valley below us as we walked along. When we finally joined the approach track again, we were all in such good spirits that we decided to jog the rest of the way back to the minibus.

We'd all eaten everything we had in our packed lunches on the summit and we were well fed. Nevertheless, I decided I'd treat everyone to a drink and a cake in the café near our minibus. It was my personal way of saying thank you to the students for the great day we'd had.

The teacher in me had, of course, taken over at times, as I'd showed them features on the map, pointing out contour lines and explaining scale, to which they'd listened intently. I was especially delighted by Colin's conduct during the walk as, much to my surprise, he'd been the perfect student to take out. He'd alternated between periods of being unusually quiet to bursting with questions. At one point, he'd put into perspective how strange this experience was for the four students; he'd pointed to the newly shorn sheep along the side of the track as we'd approached Llyn-y-Foel, and with great excitement had told the others to 'Look at them goats over there.'

'They're not goats, they're "Snowdonia Sheep",' Enid had explained to everyone. 'They've been brought down from the mountaintops to lower pastures for the winter months.'

None of the students had seen sheep with their coats shorn before – a reflection of their urban backgrounds.

My enjoyment of the day continued on the journey back to the hostel. Listening to the students' banter about different moments of their day made me smile. Each seemed to be playing 'Top Trumps' with their descriptions.

Colin, of course, loved the scrambling, pointing out, 'I was brill today, wasn't I, Tom? You'll tell Little Dave, won't you, Tom?'

'It's the first thing I'll do when we get back,' I happily agreed.

Eve and Priya, with Enid's support, had coped with the mountain environment far better than I'd expected, only occasionally looking to Enid or me for reassurance. Martin had taken the day in his stride, but quickly acknowledged the beauty of the wild landscape as Eve and Priya showed off the pictures they'd taken on their phones. Each time I heard, 'This is...' followed by a description, it would then be followed by 'wow', 'brill' and even a 'boss' or 'awesome' now and again. But the best result of the day was to come later.

'Make sure you look at Martin's photos before you go home,' Enid had stressed. 'Don't forget!'

So, as we were having our drinks back in the hostel dining room, I did as Enid had instructed.

'Can I have a deco at your photos, Martin? Enid said you've got some great ones.'

But, by what must have been the twentieth out of I don't know how many photos on Martin's phone, I understood Enid's reasoning. Nearly every photo was a 'selfie'. Not because Martin was vain – far from it – but, as he explained, 'You know me mum's never been out of London, so I'm going to send all of these to her or else she won't believe I've been to such a boss place.'

January seemed to be disappearing fast and it was the third week before Alice, Eve and I found time to sit down and discuss how Eve's training diary was going, and to complete her spring term schedule. There were now

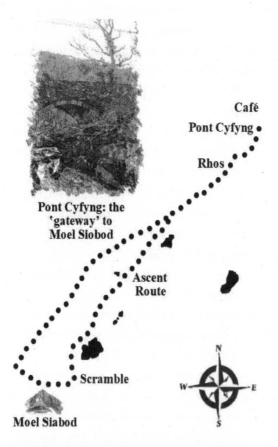

Café
Pont Cyfyng

Rhos

Pont Cyfyng: the
'gateway' to
Moel Siobod

Ascent
Route

N

W E

S

Scramble

Moel Siabod

*Route 4: Moel Siabod walk: Approximately
9 kilometres long with 678 metres' height gain.*

several students who enjoyed running, and the local residents were even getting used to a friendly 'hello' as the students ran past. It was a welcome change for the interaction between the two groups of people to be so positive. Even better, hostel staff members were giving runners more and more credit for their efforts.

Eve was following her schedule perfectly, as you'd expect. This week, her plan was to include a twenty-six kilometre run on the Saturday, before her rest day on the Sunday. What was surprising to me was the laid-back way in which she was achieving her targets. Not once did she mention any difficulties or injuries. Always with an earnest look on her face, she described to me and Alice her routes and times, which never needed amending. I was starting to realise just how outstanding she might be!

I'd now worked on two Sundays at Pen-y-Bryn, the first being our great day out on Moel Siabod. The second day was different, but just as enjoyable. We had a trek, if that's the best term to use, through Wepre Park. On this occasion the pouring rain made it all the better. I'd teamed up with Simon and we were taking eight students with us. Simon had no concerns about getting wet or muddy, and his enthusiasm was infectious. As soon as Little Dave had suggested that I join Simon on an adventure day, I'd started to look forward to it. I was already somewhat broken in by Simon's impromptu 'Winter Survival Day' in December. His adventure days were legendary with students and staff alike, and for good reason. In the past, a number of staff had made the mistake of underestimating the 'adventure' part of the day. They now belonged to a paltry group who'd refused to go out with Simon again, usually summing it up by declaring, 'Never again' or 'You're joking'. But I was actually looking forward to it.

After a grand feast of toast and tea, provided by the Pen-y-Bryn staff, we were fully prepared for the adventure that lay ahead. Just as we were about to leave the dining room, my new 'best friend forever' Colin joined us. Ever since the Moel Siabod outing, Colin had taken every opportunity he could to retell the day's highlights. Staff usually avoided taking Colin off the premises for more than a morning or afternoon because of his possible negative effect on others in the group. However, as I was Colin's BFF now, and Simon was also involved, the usual risks were considerably lessened.

Colin made a polite but quick apology to Simon for delaying the start of the day.

'Sozz, Simon, I need Tom a minute before we can go.'

Then he whisked me away to the laundry room, the aroma of soap powder and conditioner getting stronger the nearer we got to its location.

Here, he searched through the newly cleaned and ironed clothes in the 'spares cupboard', before passing me some appropriately sized grey jogging bottoms and a faded black hoodie, as well as a pair of old and worn training shoes which had actually belonged to him, though for some unexplained reason they were several sizes too big for his feet. I now knew why he'd quizzed me on my clothes' sizes as we'd hurried along the corridors to the laundry room.

Acting like a member of the care staff, rather than the cared for, he pointed out, with empathy, 'You can't wear decent stuff on a Simon day out.'

'Whatever you say, Colin,' I replied to his expert advice and quickly changed.

The ten of us set off towards the Brynford crossroads, the minibus slicing its way through the pouring rain. After what seemed like a brief twenty-four minutes, we pulled up in a small, isolated lay-by, not far from the main A55 carriageway. From here, we walked the short distance to Ewloe Castle, which lies at the south-west edge of Wepre Park. Then Simon gathered us around, so that the rules of the 'adventure' could be set out by him:

1. We were to stay in sight of Simon at all times.
2. We were to work as a team.
3. We were to help and look out for each other.
4. We were to be quiet.

I was amazed at how each rule was accepted so readily by the students, and I internally applauded the power Simon had over the group. He was like an SAS commander preparing his squad prior to a mission.

Colin put his hand on my shoulder and whispered, 'Sound, it's "follow the leader".'

As we quietly set off down the path, on the left-hand side of the stream, towards Connah's Quay, I wondered what I'd let myself in for. Everyone was following the rules to the letter so seriously and so accurately. Then, just as I was starting to feel relaxed, and I was wondering what actually made Simon's adventures so special, Simon slowly raised his right hand, making a fist as he did so. He went down on one knee and signalled to everyone to copy his position. Then he turned directly right, off the path, down a short steep slope and proceeded to walk, knee-deep, across the six-metre-wide stream.

Once on the other side, he motioned to Peter (who was allowed off-site for activities again) and gave him the number-two position behind himself. As we followed Simon, the feeling of excitement was clear on the faces of the entire group: the adventure had begun!

As I splashed into the stream, in my position as 'tail-end Charlie', I looked with pleasure at the friendly faces waiting for me on the other side. I now felt confident to be around them, whether on or off the main sites. As well as Colin, who'd taken up the position directly in front of me, my running team of Eve, Priya, Martin and Peter were there too. The other members of the squad were Dan, Chris and Stephen.

Dan was a perfect example of the condition 'hyperactivity' – even more so than Colin! If it hadn't been an existing term, then he would have caused the need for its introduction into our vocabulary. Possibly the word *Dan*peractivity' would now be a familiar term!

A common characteristic of certain classifications of special needs students is that they're undersized for their age. Even among the students at Ysgol Abaty, Dan was small compared with the others – except when standing next to Colin. With his blond locks and round National Health glasses, he looked like he was a reincarnation from the 1960s. If he'd been given a cowboy hat, he'd have been the perfect image of the 'Milkybar Kid' from that era. Without intentional malice, he'd managed to get himself permanently excluded from seven schools, including three special ones. One of the reasons for this (possibly in common with Colin) was the lack of realisation that such miniature packages could require so much high-level input from everyone.

Chris was another one of the students from *Wren*, and like many at Pen-y-Bryn he'd been in and out of care homes and hostels for the majority of his life as he didn't have any close family. Having to change residence usually wasn't his own choice or fault. Some of the homes had closed and others had merged, resulting in children needing to be placed elsewhere. This is far more common than many people outside the system realise. It usually happens due to financial decisions made by those managing the homes, which include local authority professionals and private care home managers. Being of average height and weight, and with no striking features, Chris was one of those students, like Eve, who could blend into any of their peer groups and make you wonder why they weren't in mainstream education. As we'd chatted to each other on the way to Ewloe, Chris had confided in me, 'My bestest "home" was burnt down and I had to run out in me pyjamas!'

This was the consequence of one of the students not liking the place. Chris, and everyone else, had been lucky to get out without any injuries or worse. He was even moved once simply because of his age. He knew how to 'work the system', though, when it came to both students and staff. He'd even acquired three 'substitute' siblings along the way – two sisters and a brother. All had been in previous homes with him and he'd kept in touch with them via social media on a regular basis.

Stephen, the last member of the squad, had celebrated his sixteenth birthday on Boxing Day, or Saint Stephen's Day (hence his name). In appearance, he was a stretched version of Dan and Chris. At just under six feet tall, he was willowy in build. Stephen was one of those children who was just unlucky, by order of his birth. His mother and father were still together and had nine children, all of them theirs. Stephen, along with one brother aged thirteen and a sister aged fifteen, had been put into care a few years earlier by their parents – a decision they'd made in order to reduce the number of dependants living with them from six to three at that time. But within five years, his parents had six children living at home again. However, they conveniently forgot about the three they'd already passed into the care system.

Simon seemed to have an amazing ability to balance 'exciting adventure' with 'health and safety'. By the end of our covert patrol, we'd crawled through two metres of an old, sixty centimetre diameter drainage pipe, crossed the stream again by using the underside of one of the bridges as 'monkey bars' to avoid getting our feet wet this time, and worked as a team to get everyone over a fence without actually touching it. When we arrived back at

Pen-y-Bryn, we were wet, dirty, tired, hungry and full of tales of the adventures we'd enjoyed together.

During the adventure, Simon's conversations with me had confirmed that he was naturally good at all sports and had a passion for outdoor activities. He was well qualified with nationally accredited certificates such as the SPLA (Single Pitch Lead Assessment) and MLA (Mountain Leaders' Training: both Summer and Winter). But it was the seemingly effortless way in which he managed the students that impressed me the most.

Chapter Eight

The Cross-Country Competition

B y the start of February, I was fully settled into my roles at Ysgol Abaty and Pen-y-Bryn, and during lunchtime on a Tuesday I was managing the running club that I'd established. Fortunately, the school's timetable allowed all-day staff members, as well as students, to have an hour for their lunch. This was achieved by some of the hostel staff who, having worked the previous night, finished their shift at the end of lunchtime.

Many other schools in North Wales had actually reduced their lunch period, in the hope that it would lessen the students' opportunities to get into mischief. Some schools elsewhere are even removing the lunch period altogether by having what's often known as a continental day, but thankfully the school day at Ysgol Abaty allowed the regular running session to take place within my working day, rather than after school, on most occasions. It allowed time for those who were interested to have a quick bite to eat, change and get a forty minute run in before the start of the afternoon lessons.

Ysgol Abaty couldn't have been in a better location for cross-country practice runs. In just two minutes, you could be through the school's old, rusted gates and into the Basingwerk Abbey grounds. Once in the Strand Woods, you had a choice of straight hill runs, height gains, off-track sections or Fartlek training: perfect!

There was a regular group of students who, without fail, trained every week. These were Eve, Martin, Peter and Colin. In addition, Priya and Dan attended if the weather was fine, and with one or two others, it usually meant that eight to ten students were training at every session.

Members of staff also made guest appearances. Simon and Enid would join us if the atmosphere back at the school allowed for this and, like Priya and Dan, if the weather was nice. Alice would also make an appearance from time to time.

If alone, I'd state that ten was the maximum number of students allowed to train, but this often resulted in one of the other staff members joining the group anyway, due to the reduction in the number of students on-site. This made me very popular with the other staff working on Tuesday lunchtimes, which paid dividends when a student was difficult to manage. Non-teaching staff in particular appreciated the additional time and effort I was putting in and responded by making themselves available if ever I needed their assistance, even at a moment's notice.

The next event on our fixture calendar was the Special Schools Cross-Country Competition. A number of circumstances had led to the event being held on February 14th. This was unfortunate as, like Christmas, birthdays and other celebratory days, Saint Valentine's Day often meant that the students experienced too much excitement beforehand, and too much disappointment afterwards.

I was looking forward to preparing for the competition, as well as watching the event itself. The progress I'd made in my time at Ysgol Abaty filled me with new-found confidence and I was enjoying my teaching more than ever. I'd formed excellent relationships with nearly all of the students. I was particularly pleased that Alan and Joe had settled down in my lessons and that they turned up for training sessions now and again. They were definitely two students to keep the peace with.

Like Alan, Joe had started at Ysgol Abaty after I had. Something I'd learned to come to terms with was the changing population of the students. Even having accepted it, I still found it frustrating that, often without warning, a student for whom you'd prepared a lesson would no longer be at the school. Likewise, equally frustrating was a class turning up with a student that you knew absolutely nothing about.

Joe's arrival had been known about in advance. He'd been brought to the staff members' attention during the first staff meeting in April the previous year, and all the staff were expecting his arrival sometime during the summer term. He'd actually arrived the following September. He was of dual heritage, with a white father from Wrexham and a black mother from Brazil. I loved his natural sense of humour. The first time I took him on a trip to Flint, he'd paused at a local hardware shop called Bevan's.

'What's the hold-up now, Joe?' I'd enquired.

'I'm looking at this good-looking lad,' he'd quickly replied.

When I looked in the window myself, I saw it was a mirror he was gazing into.

It was obvious to me, from the very first training session they attended together, that Eve and Joe got on well. They were both natural athletes with a gift for running. Joe's competitive nature soon saw him keeping up with Eve, mainly on Eve's short runs. Though, the first time he agreed to be her training partner, he didn't realise what he was letting himself in for. Eve's looks, rather than her running prowess, had been the main attraction for him, I think. Twenty minutes later, red faced and gasping for breath on the old railway line from Greenfield to Holywell, all he could do was look on in admiration. Eve wasn't one to change her route or pace for anyone. She was extremely polite, though, as she ran on up the hill, shouting, 'Wait here, Joe, I'll be back soon.'

By the time Eve and Joe arrived back at the start, Eve had an admirer, and I had another keen and competent runner.

Whether it was Joe's competitive nature or his desperation to impress Eve, I don't know, but by the second week in February, he was attending every

Tuesday training session. Then, when he thought he was ready to keep pace with Eve, he joined her on some of her runs. He even spent some of his free time Fartlek training, which he really enjoyed. I watched him running, in preparation for the cross-country race, around the course he'd set for himself on the rolling land around Pen-y-Bryn, and I knew that, with Eve as well, success on February 14th was looking highly probable.

Two days before the cross-country competition, Alice, Simon, Enid and I had to select the final team members. From our early beginnings, when Alice and I had tried out Eve's running ability on the Clogwyn Manod above Capel Curig, to taking the team of four to the Pensarn 16, I was now in a position where I could select a running team from a genuine squad.

The list of events that could be entered on February 14th was almost endless. Not only were there age and distance categories, but physical and mental ability were taken into account. The last race of the day was always the 'Open Team Event' where teams were made up of anyone and everyone, providing great enjoyment and amusement – even students in wheelchairs could take part. There was always some part of the course that was terribly muddy at this time of the year. With hindsight, I thought there should have been an award for the cleanest team or, even better still, the muddiest!

With the exception of the Open Team Event, where the emphasis was on fun, every other race contributed to a points system, which was taken extremely seriously. The school with the lowest points total took home the

Betsi Cadwaladr[6] Shield, as the first finishers got the lowest scores. The shield would then be displayed proudly in their school's entrance hall until the next year.

Even among the staff from the same school, there was competition. The Key Stage 3 squad was traditionally looked after by the non-teaching staff. This year, as usual, it was Simon, with Enid volunteering to help. Alice and I had taken on the task of managing the Key Stage 4 squad, for whom we had high expectations. So, as well as there being competition between the various schools, there was also in-house competition as well. For example, Ysgol Abaty staff against Pen-y-Bryn staff.

In addition, because there were so many events taking place, Alice and I each took responsibility for a particular gender: Alice took charge of the girls and I took charge of the boys. So, there was even a competitive edge between us.

The potential stars of the KS4 squad were Eve, of course, who'd already proven herself to be an exceptional runner against far stronger competition than I expected to turn up here, and Joe. Although Joe wasn't up to Eve's standard, the extra training he'd put in prior to the event meant that the times he was recording were excellent. I was confident that he'd beat any other male competitor from the Special Schools in North Wales.

On the way to the event, in positions of trust, Joe and Roy occupied the double seat alongside the driver at the front of the minibus. So, as I drove the minibus along the A55, I was treated to one of the best comedy double acts you could ever wish for, as they discussed how they might get on in their races.

'I expect you'll beat me today with your genes,' Joe commented to Roy, with his usual light-hearted banter.

'Wa' do yous mean, lah?' was the reply.

'All Scousers are good runners, cos the police are always chasing them,' quipped Joe.

'Dat's true and de bussies 'avnt nicked me yet.'

'How far have you run from the coppers then?' probed Joe.

Roy put the index finger of his right hand on the front of his chin, mimicking deep thought.

'Umm… ay went from Chester to Wrexham, so dat makes me an international, dun it. Wa' about yous?'

'I got as far as Iceland,' was Joe's remarkable reply.

'Cer, dats impressive – it's a long way.'

'About a mile, ya divvy,' Joe answered, laughing. 'Iceland's shop in Holywell, not Iceland the country.'

Eve and Joe were well supported by the other members of my squad. These included Priya, Bethan, Martin, Peter, Colin, Roy, Alan, Chris, Stephen, Michael, Dan (who, by attending every training session, had matured into another excellent runner) and not forgetting Yorkie, whose real name was Sean. Sean came from Wilmslow in Cheshire. This, with his 'posh' accent, consistent good behaviour, polite manners, as well as not being as 'street wise' as the other students, had resulted in him being called 'Yorkie' by the students – as he was 'good, rich and thick', in their opinion. Surprisingly, Sean was happy to be called Yorkie by everyone as several of the 'top dog' students had nicknames and he felt this gave him increased significance within the student population. I would have loved to have entered more students into the day's competitions, but I was limited to eighteen people in total – the number of seats on our new 2.2 litre, six-gear, Ford Transit bus.

Each year, the cross-country competition would move location, as different schools took responsibility for arranging it. This year, it was to be held in the extensive grounds of Bodelwyddan Castle, a Grade II listed building between St Asaph and Abergele.

As we turned off the road and drove through the castellated gates, I mentioned that the last time I'd been here was to have afternoon tea. The faces of the students were full of wonder, as I described this experience:

'Imagine a selection of finger sandwiches, scones with cream and strawberry preserve, Welsh cakes, *bara brith*[7] and rich shortbread, a mini selection of pastries and cakes, and a choice of traditional and herbal teas. All served in such a marvellous setting.'

With mouths watering at the thought, we all decided that we should have a *Wordsworth* outing to the tea room at a future date.

'Don't forget about me,' Enid added quickly.

Sadly, we weren't going to be inside enjoying the luxury high tea on this occasion and, instead, as I parked the minibus there was a chill in the air and light rain began to fall.

The students, from all the schools, were huddled in their minibuses, not wanting to get out and, to make things worse, everyone from Ysgol Abaty was complaining about the 'no eating' rule on the bus, regardless of the fact that it was nowhere near lunchtime.

'Why can't we?'

'It's not fair.'

'They're eating in their bus!'

'Please, Tom, no one will know...'

One or two of the staff from each of the vehicles had ventured out to discuss the weather and to set up the final course markers. Perhaps they also wanted to get away from a similar barrage of whinges.

Rhys Jones from Ysgol Weirglodd looked stressed as he flitted from one member of staff to another. He'd arrived before 9:00am in order to arrange the courses and was worried that, because of the overnight downpour, the muddy area at the bottom of the field was even worse than usual. He'd decided that one circuit of the field, which lay below the formal gardens and wooded area, would be the course for KS3 students. The KS4 students would complete three laps of the same course. This would be in keeping with health and safety, by avoiding the worst of the mud during the serious races. He would include the 'quagmire' section for the final 'fun' race of the day. So, distances were now known – two kilometres and six kilometres respectively.

Although the course was in clear view of the castle, half a dozen members of staff were sent out to key positions to ensure that the correct route was adhered to – there were to be no shortcuts! They would also be close by in case of accidents or 'ungentlemanly' tactics on the part of the students.

Rhys was now hurriedly handing out score cards to various staff members. These had relevant letters and numbers on them. He instructed the staff in their duties; they had simply to match letters to categories: KS3 = Key Stage 3; KS4 = Key Stage 4; and M = Merit (which was for those students who showed exceptional merit in being able to complete their course). There were also ascending numbers on the cards, so that the first KS3 student to finish would be given a card with 'KS3 1' on it, the second KS3 student to finish would get 'KS3 2' and so on. The length of the explanation that Rhys was giving to the staff, and the detail he was going into, would have made any onlookers wonder about the kind of special needs the staff had!

Then, with perfect timing, there was a break in the rain and, finally, the students escaped into the fresh morning air. Following words of instruction and encouragement, and after a quick warm-up, competing KS3 boys and girls, were lined up and quickly set off on their course. Ten minutes later and the KS4 boys and girls were away. Finally, those who wanted to try and complete the course, with support if required, were also heading down towards the field.

When the last competitor had completed their course, I felt that the day had been a successful one for all of those involved. Ysgol Abaty, as I'd hoped, had won the KS3 and KS4 cups. In fact, the first two KS4 places for both boys and girls were won by Ysgol Abaty students. Eve had been true to her form, finishing ahead of everyone but, in true special school tradition, all competing students were given a medal. Some students were proudly wearing them around their necks, and were able to show them off to the disappointingly low number of attending onlookers, while others were embarrassed and had stashed their medals in their pockets.

The Betsi Cadwaladr Shield was given to the overall winners – Ysgol Abaty. Interestingly, there were a few discussions among the KS4 boys and some of the staff as to whether, in future, the fastest KS4 competitor should get a shield of their own to keep. This was, no doubt, prompted by Eve's performance. It was the first year ever that a boy hadn't been the quickest runner. I don't know what would be the worst thing for some of the KS4 lads – not being the fastest or being beaten so easily by a girl?

Eve's finishing time? Well, Mair, the teaching assistant who came with Rhys, recorded twenty-one minutes and twenty-five seconds on her stopwatch. I know Rhys didn't use a trundle wheel to check his estimated two kilometre lap, but I was informed by other staff members that 'Rhys' distances are pretty spot on'.

Wanting to take full advantage of the wonderful setting, we'd decided to have our packed lunches in the castle grounds, but before I'd let anyone back on the minibus to retrieve their lunch, I moved the bus to the lower end of the car park. Although the sides of the bus clearly displayed the words 'Ysgol Abaty Special School', it seemed unethical to take up a disabled parking space for any longer than was necessary – especially with the physically proficient group that I had with me.

While we were all tucking into our packed lunches, the other school vehicles started to set off and we gave their passengers a cheery wave. Surprisingly, before getting into his own car, Rhys made a point of coming over to me. Always appearing taller than his actual six foot two inches of height – his mop of curly blond hair adding at least an inch, if not two – and always dressed in a tracksuit for sporting fixtures, Rhys could easily fit into any sporting gathering as a competitor or a coach.

As I stood up to greet him, he shook my hand and looked at Eve.

'Do you know how good she is?' he said, but before I'd decided on the best answer to give, he made it clear that his question was rhetorical. 'She's *very good*!'

The way he stressed 'very good' somehow implied far more than it normally would and left me beaming as we waved Rhys away.

A phone call to the manager of the castle the day before (and some emotional leverage about special needs children) had gained everyone from Ysgol Abaty free access to the castle with its museum and art gallery. The grounds, including two hundred and sixty acres of park and woodland, an aviary and a maze, are wonderful. I thought the students would, in particular, seek out the 'trenches' from the First World War. But, on a day like this one, with the showers starting again and the wind getting chillier, going inside the castle was the favoured choice after lunch.

Inside Bodelwyddan Castle the students had a long

discussion about how it was possible that one of the shoes in an oil painting could always point in their direction, no matter where they stood in the room. A few had taken photos in the Victorian Games Room, where it appeared as if their head, separated from their body, lay on a silver platter. (In reality, a hidden hole had been made in the platter on the table top, and a long tablecloth concealed their body underneath.) As they laughed together and shared their own unique kind of chatter, Alice and I exchanged glances and half-smiles. As experienced staff members, we knew the full-smile would have to wait until we'd got them all the way back to school.

As I drove the minibus back to school, the students discussed the highlights of their day. Although everyone was happy, Alan seemed to be the one who felt most pleased. More of an Olympic weightlifter in physique than a runner, not only had he completed the course without any walking, he'd been a member of the winning Open Team. I'd lent Alan on a 'free temporary transfer' basis to Ysgol Weirglodd to strengthen their numbers. Approaching the muddy section of the course, he'd lifted Seren, one of their KS3 students, still in her wheelchair, up to his chest. He'd then traipsed through the quagmire without even getting the wheelchair's wheels muddy – a tactic that a few of the other male wheelchair assistants had attempted but none of them had succeeded in accomplishing.

We arrived back at Ysgol Abaty just as the remaining students were climbing onto their hostel transport. Our running team was keen to show off the team shield to the school staff and any others who were around. Yet amidst all the excitement, Rhys' simple comment about Eve being 'very good' was still in the forefront of my mind.

Chapter Nine
Contrasts: The Eisteddfod and The Sawmill

The first day of March is the meteorological start of spring in the northern hemisphere. More importantly, in Wales, it's Saint David's Day or *Dydd Gŵyl Dewi*. On this day, throughout Wales, you'll find daffodils on display and Welsh dragons flying in most nooks and crannies. Primary school children will set off to school, proudly showing off their national dress costumes. The feeling of national patriotism is everywhere; even special schools are taken over by it.

In schools, this day usually starts off with a Welsh assembly. If this isn't possible, the timetable will often be relaxed to allow the classes to devote their first lesson to a Welsh theme. Ysgol Abaty was no exception to this rule, with our head teacher Gareth being the chief promoter of *Dydd Gŵyl Dewi*. I was lucky enough to have *Wordsworth* as my form class on this day. So, I started my week with a relaxing telling of the story of Saint David, the patron saint of Wales.

Following the first lesson with their form teachers, all the students were gathered together for an Eisteddfod, which is a celebration of the Welsh language and culture, notably through poetry, drama and music. This event took place in the original dining room of the old Victorian house. As it was the room with the largest floor area, it was often used for school gatherings, and it was also the only indoor area where all the students and staff could come together in one place.

As many of the students had a statement of special educational needs, as well as coming from counties outside Wales, the Ysgol Abaty Eisteddfod was always a casual affair. Modern Welsh music was played, such as the singer Duffy's work, and food was served, such as *bara brith* and Welsh cakes. Many of the staff wore daffodils, a custom that's based on the legend that St David required Welsh soldiers to wear leeks when they went into battle against the Saxons, so that they'd be able to tell who was friend and foe. As daffodils and leeks share the same Welsh name, *cennin*, daffodils tend to be more popular as a symbol to wear nowadays, because of their pretty appearance and, unlike leeks, their pleasant scent!

Gareth took great pride in organising the Eisteddfod. He'd grown up on the Isle of Anglesey, or '*Ynys Môn*, the mother of Wales' as he always called it. He was from a strong Welsh background and the Eisteddfod was a particular passion of his. As a fluent Welsh speaker and a patriot, he attended the National Eisteddfod every year. In reality, Gareth was as patriotic and as proud a

Welshman as you are ever likely to meet.

True to form, Gareth had set a calendar of events in preparation for the school Eisteddfod, which he'd asked all the staff to follow. This had started straight after Christmas when Jane Harris, the Art teacher, had presented all the students with the challenge of producing a 'Welsh' piece of artwork. This was usually in the form of a painting, with the KS3 students having the most enthusiasm for this particular task.

Unsurprisingly, this year's winner was Michael, who'd copied a photograph of Snowdon that Enid had taken back in December, viewed from the Capel Curig area. It clearly showed the Snowdon Horseshoe, with its snow-capped mountains, reflected in the Llynnau Mymbyr lakes. Jane had printed out an A3 copy of the original picture for Michael. He'd traced over it, by holding it up to the window to make sure the basic outlines showed through, and then he'd painted it in watercolours in his own impressive style. It would have compared well with the work of any other talented KS3 artist.

Several staff members would perform sketches or songs during the Eisteddfod, usually humorous ones, with a Welsh theme. This year, the most unforgettable performance was by Enid and Simon, who acted out the Welsh classic 'Baby its Cold Outside'[8]. It was a parody of Tom Jones and Cerys Matthews' performance of their 1999 Christmas single. Simon would have blended in well with the local farmers attending the animal auction in St Asaph, especially as he'd obtained a thick black wig and a flat cap for the occasion. But it was Enid in her over-the-top Welsh accent and slightly risqué Welsh lady's fancy dress outfit who really stole the show. She would have blended in well with the girls from the South Wales' Valleys on a hen night, touring 'Chippy Lane' and the surrounding pubs in Cardiff. By the volume of applause from the audience, they easily won the staff competition.

More in keeping with the true character of the Eisteddfod, the serious performances by the students included a solo rendition of the Welsh national anthem, *'Hen Wlad Fy Nhadau'* ('Old Land of My Fathers'), by Colin, in perfect tune. His performance of 'Delilah' had been my initial introduction to Ysgol Abaty, but his climbing prowess, with a total disregard for his own safety, had distracted me at the time from acknowledging his superb singing voice. Now, appearing almost angelic, I suddenly saw a side of Colin I hadn't come across before. Gareth endorsed my praise and added that Colin's Welsh pronunciation had been *bendigedig* (or 'wonderful').

As soon as the Eisteddfod had finished, the students were divided up into their separate class groups and dispersed back to their normal classrooms as quickly as possible. It had been a great event, especially when you consider that the vast majority of the students didn't have a Welsh background. So, the last thing the staff members wanted now was to tempt fate by keeping the whole student population, with their complicated mix of special needs, in one place for any longer than was necessary.

By 4:40pm, the Eisteddfod already seemed an age ago

and as I was driving home, I became preoccupied with thoughts of my next running club session, deciding on distances and routes. This had now become a regular part of my working week due to the club's popularity with the students. I was pleasantly surprised by the commitment the club members had developed.

It was one of those miserable March lunchtimes when it would have been far easier to stay indoors in the warm and dry. Venturing out into the heavy drizzle and cold east wind for a training session was hardly appealing, and it certainly wasn't a session for hanging about for too long. So, with distances set and instructions quickly given, we all set off.

In previous sessions, I'd been able to make accurate recordings of the distances and times of the individual students. This meant that I was able to set the runners off at different intervals for their particular distances. Having slowly worked my way through the various levels, I was able to enjoy running with the penultimate group.

Eve had fully established herself as the last runner to set off and to be the one to complete the greatest distance. Sometimes she'd complete two of the shorter laps; at other times she'd simply be the last one to set off and then overtake everyone else. I'd learned that one of Eve's greatest assets was her attention to detail, and this included her timing. If she was asked to set off twenty-three seconds after the penultimate runner or group of runners, I could always be sure that it would not be twenty-two or twenty-four seconds, but twenty-three seconds exactly.

Although each Tuesday lunchtime was a 'working' one, due to the comradely banter within the squad and the shared enjoyment of running that had developed, it no longer seemed to make the day lengthy or hard work. Occasionally, a member of the hostel staff would join us – usually Enid or Simon if they were on duty. If it was a particularly large turnout, then I always asked for one of the hostel staff to take part. Depending on who was on duty, this could involve a great deal of rumination, as not all of the hostel staff were keen on the idea of going out for a run in all weathers.

On a few occasions, Alice would join us. When this happened, she would have talked several of the girls into taking part. This was always when the weather was a lot more pleasant than it was today though, as Alice was definitely a fair-weather runner.

Later, when tidying up at the end of the day, I acknowledged what a great Tuesday it had been. But I made a point of balancing this thought with the wise words of an older, more experienced member of staff:

'When in a special school and things are going well, absorb that feeling as much as you can – it won't last long!'

By the end of the second lesson of the following Friday, I was wondering what had happened to the world. My first double lesson of the day had been with *Wren*, a class of mainly hyperactive KS3 boys, who, though demanding of one's attention, always had an enthusiasm and willingness to learn. In many ways, they often reminded me of why I'd decided to take up teaching in the first place. As a class, with the right support staff, I'd always found *Wren* to be easily manageable. I'd taken them off-site on several occasions and had never had any great concerns about doing so. All in all, I was delighted with the positive relationship and trust I'd nurtured with them.

This morning I was timetabled to teach *Wren* English, but I'd decided to take the boys out with me, as a positive but realistic 'advert' for the school, when I visited a local timber manufacturer, Coastal Wood Products, based in Bagillt near Holywell. The business produces timber buildings, including large log cabins. They export their products throughout the world, including to some Scandinavian countries, which speaks volumes about their high standards. Fortunately, they also donated offcuts from their creations to the school, keeping the Ysgol Abaty's wood store fully stocked.

I'd set myself two objectives for my morning visit. The first was to acquire as much spare wood as I could, thereby allowing me to balance my materials budget better. I hoped that the money I might save on timber could be spent instead on specialist parts for the students' creations – for example, clock movements, pyrography wood-burning pens and so on. These were the sort of resources that allowed students to produce worthwhile products quickly and often with little skill.

My second objective was to investigate the possibility of some work experience placements for students for the following year – especially for Chris who would then be in *Shakespeare*. Chris had impressed me the very first time I taught him. I was always surprised that he hadn't settled in at any of the previous schools he'd attended, while moving between the many children's homes he'd inhabited. Whenever I thought of Chris, I realised just how unfair life could be. It was with this thought in mind that I'd decided to go out of my way to try and find Chris a positive work placement.

Although the class had been unusually boisterous on arrival, when I explained to them the purpose of the morning's outing, they seemed to calm down from the 'high' they were on. I thought that avoiding having *Wren* in a workshop, full of tools and resources that could cause serious, even deadly, harm, was a wise move when they were in a 'boisterous' mood, and the idea of an outing was made even more realistic by the fact that Simon was covering for Imre H, one of the LSAs who also worked in Pen-y-Bryn. Imre H's wife Szófia, who was known by many of the students, was expecting to give birth to their first child sometime during the day. All of the students and staff were aware of this and looked forward to the happy event.

I decided to drive the minibus, with Simon sitting in the back 'riding shotgun', as we always referred to it. As I drove through the school gates, the conversation between the students was already louder than normal and sounded like it was on a vexing audio loop.

'You move.'

'No, you move.'

'I always sit there.'

'Not now, you don't!'

Simon moved from empty seat to empty seat to sit between various students, trying to keep a lid on things.

We arrived at Coastal Wood Products just as the clock on the dashboard showed 9:30am. Once everyone was quiet, I reminded the class of why we were here.

'This is where I'll get the wood for all the great things you'll make this year, and if we're lucky Chris will also get his work experience here when he's in *Shakespeare*.'

With the students pondering this information, I left Simon to look after them and made my way across the timber yard. The fumes of freshly cut wood, with its accompanying scent of burnt sawdust, greeted me as I entered the workshop door. I carefully made my way to the door marked 'Manager' to introduce myself properly to the manager Mike Williams. Up to this point, I'd only ever talked to him on the phone.

I'd only just finished introducing myself, and was about to raise the question of work experience for Chris, when Yorkie came rushing into Mike's office.

Turning towards him, I asked, 'What is it, Sean?'

He tried to compose himself and announced as politely as he could, 'Excuse me, sir, Simon would like you to return to the bus now, if that's convenient?' Then he was gone again.

Mike looked at me, his puzzlement clear.

'I'm sorry, Mike,' I said, 'you'll have to excuse me... I'd better go and see what's going on.'

Knowing Yorkie's reputation for never messing about, I made a speedier exit from Mike's office than I'd planned and followed Yorkie in the direction of the minibus.

As I rounded the corner of the prefabricated sawmill, I could see Simon with a few of the boys gathered around him. Some were laughing, some were swearing, and some were doing both. They were next to a forklift truck. Its engine was running and its forks were raised almost as high as the overhead guard. To my utter dismay and dread, Chris was in the driving seat!

During the five minutes or so when I'd tried to develop a positive and lasting relationship between Ysgol Abaty and Coastal Wood Products, my chosen group of students had more than managed to shift Mike's opinion in a completely different direction. This was confirmed as I heard Mike's voice, from behind me, echoing around the small industrial estate.

'Get off that machine now!'

The only surprise to me was that Mike hadn't included any swear words in this instruction.

Apparently, as soon as I was out of sight of the minibus, the quarrels in the bus had magnified greatly. Surprisingly, most were fuelled by comments from Chris, including:

'I thought we were having a day out – this place is fucking shit.'

When Chris' insults finally made Michael reach the end of his tether, he landed a solid punch on the side of Chris' head before Simon had time to intervene. Simon did manage to prevent Michael's second punch landing, by getting his own body in the way. While holding on to

Michael's seat, he created a safe space between Michael and Chris. Simon now found himself fully occupied with Michael and the rest of the group, who all wanted to play their part in the growing mayhem – the 'domino effect' was in full flow. No surprises there then!

This had allowed Chris time to exit the minibus via the rear door. Then, in well under the sixty seconds estimated for stealing a car in the 2000 film *Gone in 60 seconds*, starring Nicholas Cage and Angelina Jolie, Chris had hot-wired a secured forklift and was trying to drive it around between the neatly arranged stacks of timber on the yard.

All of those years spent in special schools and children's homes had provided Chris with many specialist skills – how to hot-wire a vehicle being one of these. For Chris, starting the forklift was 'easy pickings', but controlling it wasn't so easy. However, he was managing to drive it backwards and forwards at high speeds, narrowly avoiding knocking over several of the timber stacks in the process.

Before I had time to head them off, two of the timber yard workers arrived on the scene.

'Get the fuck off that fucking truck now!' reverberated around the yard.

The worker was clearly not a member of management.

Unfortunately for all concerned, especially me – as he was within a metre or so of where I was standing – the source of the bellowing was the larger of the two workmen. Probably in his mid-thirties, he was dressed in boots, jeans and a padded shirt. His shirt's striking red and black tartan of the Munro clan, as well as his impressive build – that of the preverbal 'brick shit house' – brought to mind a scene from *Braveheart* and I could easily imagine him saying, 'They will never take our forklift!'

With some creative thinking, the scene that was unfolding could possibly be viewed as an example of group bonding. For, as soon as the students realised that Chris was being 'disrespected', their differences were completely forgotten. They all dashed to Chris' defence and gathered around the forklift. Unfortunately, this involved picking up some lengths of spare timber and using every swear word available to them to threaten the two workmen as they approached.

Simon, who by now had positioned himself between the boys and the workmen, was managing to block the path of Michael, who seemed to have forgotten his personal differences with Chris and was now ready to defend him to the death. Michael was busy exchanging insults, swear words and instructions with both of the workmen. It was only two minutes earlier that he'd wanted to 'rip Chris' fucking head off', as he'd put it.

By now, I'd also managed to step into the path of the two workmen. Fortunately, they slowed their pace when they realised that their verbal protests hadn't had the intimidating effect on the group that they'd hoped for. In fact, the opposite effect had resulted.

There have been few times in my life when I've felt the need to freeze, as if to let my mind have time to make a decision, and this was definitely one of them. Luckily, everyone around me seemed to be in the same time-slip. As I restarted my own clock and made my way closer to Chris, with telepathic symmetry, Simon was doing the same thing towards Michael. As Chris was now off the forklift and Mike Williams was on the case, the workmen seemed to have decided to become part of the audience rather than the performance.

Chris was now goading the workers with, 'What are they fucking looking at now? I got off, didn't I?'

Realising that Michael was going to be the easier of the two ringleaders to pacify, I directed a calm proposal at him, making sure that Chris would hear it too:

'If you're going to swear at them, at least show your intelligence and use a three-syllable swear word!'

This had the desired effect of pausing Michael's barrage of swearing.

Then Colin, with perfect timing, provided the final action that defused the situation, when he declared:

'Leave it, Chris, yous going to get Tom and Simon into piles of shit when we get back to school.'

With Yorkie already back on the bus (an action he took independently), the rest of *Wren* followed, apart from Colin, Chris and Michael. Michael, no doubt, was pleased and relieved to have received the 'get me out of this situation' card from Colin.

Michael then quickly backed up Colin's statement, 'It's not worth it, Chris, like yous sez – this place is shit.'

Without talking, the three boys made their way to the bus and sat down in their seats. I had to make a 'walk of shame' to Mike as he stood there waiting for me to cross back over the yard to him.

'I'm sorry about the boys' behaviour; I don't know what happened,' I said, and bit my tongue before saying 'They were fine when I was with them' as this was totally untrue and not at all fair on Simon. 'I'll get them back to school and phone you later. If there's any damage to the forklift, please let me know,' I added in as friendly a tone as I could manage.

Mike's reply, which wasn't in a friendly tone, was simply, 'Phone me later.' Then he walked back inside past the two workmen who appeared to be waiting for round two.

Twenty minutes later, Simon and I, as well as the students, were back on the minibus heading through the gates of Ysgol Abaty. I'd decided not to ask Mike, 'When would you be able to deliver the free wood?' It had seemed inappropriate to bring it up in our parting conversation. As did, 'When might it be possible for Chris to start his work experience with you?'

That evening, Simon and I spent the best part of an hour filling in the required 'incident forms'. We then spent a further half an hour discussing the events with Chris, after which we were able to reach the following conclusions.

Although self-assured and happy in the school and hostel, Chris was, in fact, lacking in self-confidence. This had been made worse by the fact that every time he'd felt settled and secure somewhere in the past, he'd been moved on. The alarming behaviour that he'd demonstrated at Coastal Wood Products, to Simon and me, wasn't personal. Actually, he clearly felt that he'd developed some positive relationships with both of us. In his words, 'I like yous two; you're sound.' This sentiment was easily reciprocated by Simon and me, due to Chris' usually easy-going nature. We discovered that Chris wasn't willing to, or able to, accept the possibility of disappointing us, especially me, on his potential work placement. I'm sure this was a response to my own high regard for him. In his mind, his only solution or 'get out plan' was to spoil the procedure. Chris had certainly done this, and in style.

Simon's final comment to me about the incident, as we were gathering our things together to leave, was:

'You know, I still can't think of a swear word with three syllables...'

Then off he went down the corridor towards *Aran*, chuckling to himself, no doubt still going through his vocabulary of curses in his head.

As I was crossing the car park to make my way home, Chris, Michael, Martin and Peter came to meet me. Eve and Priya were watching them from under the canopy at the school entrance, probably waiting at a safe distance to see what my reaction to the boys' presence would be.

'We're going running to clear our heads,' Peter called over to me.

I'd mentioned 'clearing your head' on an earlier training session, as one of the many bonuses that running can have.

'Come with us, Tom; it's perfect weather,' Priya

added – always the peacemaker.

Only a few seconds earlier, setting off for home – and as soon as possible – had been my only aim, but my reflex action was to join them, even though Chris and Michael had been the main contributors to my day of stress. So, with Eve and Priya in tow, the seven of us set off towards the Dee Estuary Coastal Path.

During the run, we chatted about many things – except, of course, the events that had occurred earlier at the timber yard. An hour later, at 6:27pm to be precise, after an eight kilometre run in excellent company, my head had cleared, my stress levels were reduced, and I was setting off for home again.

It was 6:56pm as I passed the road sign saying *Pant* (meaning 'valley' in Welsh) where I lived, indicating that I was finally within three minutes of finishing my working day, as I always included travelling time in this. With my mind calmer, the bouquet of the spring flowers combined with the sight of the road sign brought back memories of the family joke that my two daughters and I had continually played on people throughout the spring and long hot summer of 1999 before my eldest went off to high school. It worked best with my daughters' English cousins, but also with my oldest daughter's friends when they were being driven to our home for the first time.

My daughters would point out how important it was to be aware of the signs at the side of the road. I'd slow down as we passed the 'Slow/*Araf*' signs on the bends before approaching the village. Having regained some speed, I'd then reduce it again to 30mph at the speed limit sign, often at my youngest daughter's instruction as she wanted to play her part in the approaching joke, which she found hilarious. Then, as we reached the village sign, *Pant*, we'd all start panting, much to the bewilderment of our passengers and the embarrassment of my wife, if she was with us, as she could never understand why my daughters and I always found it so funny.

Chapter Ten
The Easter Egg Hunt

When exactly are the Easter holidays? A question asked by many! It's often a mystery as to why it's on a particular date. As part of the academic year, it can also create great imbalances between the length of the spring term and also the half terms.

This year, Easter Sunday was to be on the 27th of March – one of the earliest dates on which it could fall. At the penultimate Monday staff meeting before the holiday, Imre H had suggested an idea:

'Why don't we have an Easter egg hunt to break up the mundanity of the last week? It's a great activity and the winners could have a prize – an Easter egg to share maybe, or even some individual cream eggs?'

I'd respected Imre H from the moment I'd met him; he was so knowledgeable on so many topics. Also, as well as his home language of Hungarian, he was fluent in Slovakian, English and spoke some Russian and Welsh as well.

Once the idea of the egg hunt had been accepted by all the staff as a suitable form of entertainment for the students, Imre H eagerly set about preparing for the event, as he ideally wanted it to be held on the Tuesday before Ysgol Abaty closed for the Easter holidays. The advantage of this date was that some of the KS3 students would be having a visit to a local wildlife park, so it seemed like perfect timing as it would be easier to arrange those left behind into compatible groups.

In preparation, Imre H had already, after much consideration, split those who'd be present into six groups regardless of their Key Stage. When you included staff, we realised that four groups of ten would travel on four of the six school minibuses. Two groups of five would then use the school's two 'people carriers'. This meant that there would be at least two members of staff with each group.

After showing me yet more photographs of his baby daughter Jazmin, now two weeks old, Imre H asked, 'Will you drive one of the minibuses for me, Tom?'

'No problem at all, you just tell me when and where.'

When I first realised that Ysgol Abaty and Pen-y-Bryn had six minibuses available to them, I'd thought that it was a great overspend on this particular part of the school budget. I was really taken aback when I saw vehicles with fifteen (or more) seats travelling around with only two or three students in them. It was only during my third week in the school that I discovered how full a minibus could seem with just two adults and two students inside.

On that occasion, Gareth had asked me to do him a favour during one of my non-teaching periods.

Would you go with Little Dave when he drives one of the minibuses for me today, Tom? It'd be a great help.'

As it was one of the first conversations I'd had with Gareth since my interview and I was keen to please, I cheerfully and with little hesitation replied, 'Yes, no problem at all, just tell me when.'

Apparently, Little Dave needed another member of staff to 'ride shotgun' with him when he transported two of the students from the school to the hostel. This immediately brought to mind one of the many Western films I'd enjoyed so much as I grew up in the 60s and 70s. The driver and his 'pardner' would be sitting high up on a Wells Fargo stagecoach. A shotgun, or even a Winchester rifle, would be held diagonally across the pardner's chest, for any potential outlaws to see. Dust would be billowing from the two oversized rear wheels, which mysteriously looked as if they were going in the wrong direction, as the four horses galloped on, crossing the American plains. Did this image influence my quick, positive reply to Gareth? Of course it did.

Now, with hindsight, I realise that 'riding shotgun' isn't an activity to volunteer for without thinking carefully about it. With more thought, I might have noted how many of those pardners, sitting high up on the stagecoach, usually ended up shot dead and lying face down in the dust. I also now realise that when a manager asks you if you'd like to do him a favour, like some of the cowboys from those films, he might be speaking with a 'forked tongue'. Especially if there are unnecessary added benefits being offered! On this occasion, Gareth had said, 'You can take time out from teaching, if needed, to take your car up to the hostel first, so that it's ready for you to drive back afterwards.' At the time, I'd really thought how obliging and considerate this was of Gareth.

With my own car parked at the Pen-y-Bryn car park, I got a lift from Bryn who, as our maintenance man, was forever commuting between the hostel and school sites, trying to keep up with the always increasing number of repair jobs that the students provided for him.

As I walked into Gareth's office to meet him and receive some final instructions, I was surprised to see that it was full to bursting with people. As well as Joe and Alan, who I presumed were the two students in need of transport to Pen-y-Bryn, spread around the room were Dai Twice, Little Dave, Simon, Dianne a new LSA and key worker for Joe, and, of course, Gareth. To use an old saying, there wasn't enough room to swing a cat. I learned later that this was exactly why Gareth had so many of us in one compact place – though it was probably chairs, rather than cats, that he was thinking of.

Gareth was concluding what I'm sure had been a long, drawn-out speech as I arrived.

'It's over now – you two just need to get on with each other.'

Then, with military precision, Little Dave and I, with Joe and Alan in tow, exited Gareth's office and made the short journey to the delegated minibus.

Little Dave didn't speak directly to me as we walked

along, escorting Joe and Alan. A couple of metres from the minibus, to my relief and surprise he calmly passed me the keys and indicated that he wanted me to drive.

The usual ten minute drive to Pen-y-Bryn took an extra six minutes. I was, subconsciously, making the journey as calm and gentle as possible, even allowing another driver to turn ahead of me as I approached the Brynford crossroads before turning right. My thinking must have been 'keep everything calm and peaceful outside of the minibus and it will be the same inside'. The whole journey was completed in total silence.

When we got to Pen-y-Bryn both boys got out and walked into the hostel without speaking or looking at each other. Little Dave (somehow making himself seem even taller than six foot eight inches) and I stayed a carefully measured distance behind them.

Much to my surprise, Joe and Alan hadn't caused any trouble on the minibus. However, the deep sighs that Little Dave gave as the two of them headed off to their individual rooms in *Aran* made me appreciate just how tense, and potentially explosive, the situation had been. The journey also demonstrated to me how little personal space there can be on a minibus designed for sixteen passengers, when there are only four people on board.

'Why did Gareth choose me originally to ride shotgun this time?' I remember asking Little Dave later. 'I'm sure there are far more capable staff than me around to do the job.'

He leaned forward and gently put his right hand on my left shoulder. 'You're the only male member of staff working today who's not been injured this week.'

As it was only Wednesday, it was a sobering thought, if ever there was one.

Imre H had planned the Easter egg hunt meticulously. He'd photocopied maps of the hunt area, giving detailed clues to enable the teams to find the eggs he'd concealed there. After an early-evening meal at Pen-y-Bryn, we were divided into our teams. And just two minutes after Imre H's planned time of 5:30pm, the first minibus, with its team of ten on board, drove off.

Imre H had chosen to set the teams off at five-minute intervals, though he'd also had the foresight to have the route tackled in alternate directions, which created a ten-minute gap between vehicles going off in the same direction. This still meant that the same distance and the same clues were available to everyone, thereby keeping it a fair competition.

I was part of the second team, so as soon as the first minibus was out of sight, I'd got everyone on board and we were ready to go. Even though it wasn't a timed race, my competitive streak had taken over.

I had three other staff members on the minibus with me – Simon, Enid and Alice. A mixed bunch of students completed our team of ten, including Eve, Priya, Martin, Peter and Joe. As we made our way around the lanes that surround Pantasaph, everyone took on their assigned roles with glee. For reasons that couldn't be explained, our team of ten, on this occasion, just worked.

Priya read out the directions and clues as we went

along.

'Clue one: what animal is on the sign after you pass the golf course?'

Martin and Peter took a side of the bus each, in order to look for answers to the riddles that Imre H had set.

'A horse!' shouted someone from the rear of the minibus, and this was quickly written down by Enid, before Martin jumped out and collected a cream egg from the foot of the blue-and-white bridleway signpost.

Once a 'treasure spot' was discovered and the answer to the clue recorded, some of the students leapt off the minibus to retrieve the Cadbury's Mini Eggs, which Imre H had hidden. This was to be the evidence of our find. The only conflict occurred when Joe wanted to swap one of the eggs hidden in a telephone kiosk for a 'good time' lady's card, which was tucked into the information board above the phone. The compromise, so that we could carry on with our Easter egg hunt, was that Joe could keep the card. Hopefully, only as a souvenir!

By 7:31pm, our team was back at Pen-y-Bryn, celebrating our hoard of eggs and enjoying a drink of hot chocolate, followed by endless pieces of buttered toast. The entire group made a point of telling Imre H what a great activity it had been.

At 7:57pm, Little Dave, Helen, Dianne and Tony, another new member of the hostel staff, arrived with their group. Even after nearly two terms at Ysgol Abaty, the turnover of staff still amazed me; it was really hard to keep up with their names at times.

Before I could ask Little Dave how they'd got on, and

congratulate him on completing the egg hunt and getting back safely, he declared:

'That's the worst evening I've ever had in hostel.'

As it was only just past 8:00pm – the usual time when boredom affects the students and trouble starts to brew – it was a powerful statement.

Little Dave and the other three staff members who'd been with him related the story of their trip in the minibus, breaking it up into brief time periods. Even before they'd left the Pen-y-Bryn site, arguments had broken out among the students about which roles they should adopt. By the time they'd reached the main road, the verbal arguments had turned physical, with some students demanding that they sit in particular seats or have particular roles for the event.

Whenever they reached a clue, they all wanted to get off and look for the answers. With there being several doors on the minibus, this made it almost impossible for the staff to keep control of what was going on. What was especially concerning was the fact that the students seemed to have no regard for their own safety. Several times they'd walked or run out in front of oncoming traffic, causing panic and frustration all around.

By the end of the search for the third clue (there were twelve clues in all), no one on the bus felt like carrying on with the egg hunt. It had turned into a shouting match between the students. So, the staff had made the correct decision to retire from the competition and return to Pen-y-Bryn. The journey back to Pen-y-Bryn from Brynford was made even worse by students shouting obscenities through the minibus windows, followed by rude gestures, to anyone unlucky enough to be in that particular area that evening. This would, no doubt, result in a number of phone calls being made to the school and hostel during the following day. Something else for Little Dave, Helen, Dianne and Tony to look forward to!

I wondered how the same activity could have had such differing results. One group was telling Imre H it was one of the best evenings ever, while another group was saying it was one of the worst.

My mind never seemed to wander far from running, whether I was at school or in the hostel. Even as I'd driven around the course set by Imre H, I'd been selecting new routes in my head for my more elite runners. There were three good hill road challenges in the area, which roughly linked the school and the hostel. The first was Pen y Ball Hill, the second Carmel Hill and the third Brynford Street. Each one was long enough and steep enough to test the best of any club runners. I decided to put my new routes to the test on the following Tuesday evening, as Little Dave had asked me to work overtime due to hostel staff shortages. The days were now getting warmer, allowing runs to be pleasurable once again.

We set off from Ysgol Abaty. Eve, as a solo runner, had the longest route. I'd worked out that she could go from school, past St Winefride's Well, which gives Holywell its name, then straight up Pen y Ball Hill, turn left when she reached Monastery Road, down Brynford Street, along Fron Park Road and Holway Road, then onto Carmel Hill, to finish at the monument beside Pen-y-Bryn. This was a testing route even for Eve – about thirteen kilometres long, with about four hundred and sixty metres of height gain. Depending on how she got on, I was considering a future plan for her.

The origin of my plan for Eve went back to a chance meeting I'd had on Snowdon in 1986. I've always enjoyed walking, scrambling and climbing in the mountains and had set off on a solo, winter's day walk, to take advantage of the excellent snow and ice conditions.

Choosing a weekday always reduced the number of walkers who were about. The poor road conditions, due to the recent snowfall on both the A55 and the A5 kept to a minimum travellers from a great distance and when I pulled into the park at Pen-y-Pass at 9:32am, there were only four cars parked there before me.

This was the day I first met Geraint. It was quiet on the mountain, to say the least, and with a snowline at a little over one hundred metres, Snowdon was looking as it should, with its bright white, snow-covered summit set against a deep blue sky.

My plan was to set off up the Miners' Track, join the Pyg Track and go on from there to the summit. Then, depending on the snow and ice conditions that I found on my way up, I'd either choose to retrace my footsteps or decide to make the whole of the return journey on the Pyg Path.

I reached the north-east end of Llyn Llydaw with my pulse racing far more than usual as the snow was at times thigh-high, making my progress enjoyable but hard work

**The monument that stands
near the entrance to Pen-y-Bryn Hostel.**

*Route 5: Training circuit from
Ysgol Abaty to Pen-y-Bryn: Approximately
13 kilometres long with 460 metres' height gain.*

and sluggish. A single pattern of footprints in the snow ahead of me had made my choice of route easy, and I was grateful that there was evidence of other human life in the vast white wilderness into which I'd ventured.

I took the opportunity to have a breather as I studied the splendour of the Snowdon massif in front of me. The diverse range of grey sedimentary and igneous crags stood out against the white of the snow and ice. The view was made even more vivid by the panoramic blue-sky backdrop. As I often did, I tried to capture the beauty of the scene on my compact Canon camera, knowing in reality that even the best professional photographer couldn't achieve a print that compared with being there in person and seeing the scene first-hand. The feeling of isolation made me wonder how Thomas Johnson must have felt on his first ascent of Snowdon in 1639.

'Lovely, isn't it?' seemed to materialise out of nowhere, as I was clicking away, and I suddenly became aware of someone sitting on the path about ten metres ahead of me.

His blue rucksack with its red ice axe strapped to the back was carefully placed beside him on the upper side of the slope. I glanced quickly at my own rucksack, now at rest a metre and a half lower down the slope than I was, and thought, *Why didn't I do that?*

Having taken some time to stabilise my position, I replied, 'It's a view I never tire of and today it's possibly at its finest.'

'As the name *Snow*don suggests... so it should be,' he reasoned.

We both feasted our eyes on the snow-clad landscape in silence for a few more minutes.

Just like me, he'd stopped to admire the view, take some photographs and recover from the trek he'd just made up to our current location. After some quick introductions, we were both starting to feel the cold, so we set off again, together, towards the intersection of the Pyg Track.

We quickly discovered that we had a mutual love of the mountains of North Wales, especially Snowdon. Unfortunately, the deteriorating weather on that particular day, resulting in white-out conditions at the junction of the Miners' and Pyg Tracks, prevented us from reaching the summit. However, Geraint and I went on to visit the summit of Snowdon together many times after that initial meeting. In total, with the other peaks in Wales, England and Scotland that we visited, often with friends or family, we must have summited more than one hundred mountains together.

Having gained a mutual respect for each other, it was in 1991, while sharing lunch on the summit of Tryfan, the lowest of the Welsh peaks over three thousand foot, when Geraint asked, 'Have you ever thought of doing the UMM?'

My puzzled expression no doubt indicated that I was waiting for him to remember the word he was trying to finish his sentence with.

Eventually, this prompted him to say, 'The Ultimate Mountain Marathon!'

The weather on that day was as far removed from our

first meeting as it could be. With our rucksacks propping us up as makeshift backrests, we were able to enjoy the exceptionally hot March sunshine. Our shirts were off, and the more adventurous walkers who were attempting their first leap between the rocks called Adam and Eve provided entertainment for us both.

Although only five years older than me, Geraint seemed to have had many more mountain years' experience. I'd never heard of the Ultimate Mountain Marathon or UMM as it apparently was often referred to. Geraint had completed the UMM twice before, with different partners, and he enthused about every aspect of it. 'Cunning running,' he called it!

I would have found it challenging to decline the offer, as he discussed the different adventures he'd had as part of his UMM experiences. In truth, however, it only took Geraint's opening sentences on the topic to have me 'chomping at the bit'.

I decided to take the plunge and agreed to partner Geraint on his next UMM. We had five months to prepare, which seemed more than enough. As always, the location was kept secret until about a week before the event took place. So, it was in mid-August 1992 that we learned it was to be held in the Rhinogs (*Rhinogydd*) Mountains, which are at the south-western end of Snowdonia and don't possess the high peaks of their neighbours. More isolated and less visited than the rest of North Wales, the area can allow you to walk all day without seeing anyone else. This and its captivating scenery make it an ideal location for an excursion or a mountain marathon.

After months of fitness and navigational practice, we finally took part in our first UMM together. After a minimum distance of thirty-six kilometres, and at least two thousand and sixty-five metres of altitude gain, we eventually completed the mountain marathon together. Finishing in the top third of competitors, we were justifiably pleased and proud of our success. But it was as we got out of the car on the way back from Harlech, to walk the short distance across the car park to the Chocolate House and Tearoom at Pentrefoelas, that our legs felt the reality of what we'd done. The extra weight of the required equipment, not always carried on our training sessions, had taken its toll. Slowly sitting down at one of the tables, we both wondered when we'd ever be able to stand up again.

I wasn't considering a mountain marathon event as an interesting or realistic weekend away for the students. Perhaps that might be an adventure that some of them would have in the future. It was two of the warm-ups that Geraint had used while training for our first joint mountain marathon that I thought the students would enjoy and succeed at. The first was to complete the Welsh 3000s within twenty-four hours. The second was an entry into a marathon, such as the Snowdon Marathon, which was held every year in October. But first of all, I had to decide which students would cope with this level of endurance and which would be suitable in terms of their temperament. So, the question I asked myself was, *How do I decide which students are potential mountain adventurers?*

The answer was simple really: take them up one of the Welsh 3000s – and there could be no better mountain than Snowdon for this challenge.

Chapter Eleven

A Special Sunset and Sunrise

Where possible, I followed the advice in Eric Langmuir's book *Mountaincraft and Leadership*[9]. This suggests that an ideal mountain party size is between three and ten people, and I've always found that between six and eight is the best number.

Deciding on which member of staff should partner me was easy. The day out on Moel Siabod in January had been one of the most enjoyable ones I'd had on a mountain. This was almost entirely due to Enid's contribution. So, all I had to do was ask, when next I saw her, and hope that her answer would be yes. After all, we'd become great friends, sharing a similar sense of humour and, when necessary, drawing on each other's strengths.

Our friendship had been tested, though, when Enid had encouraged me to join her for a session at her local karate club. Although a little nervous about the personal risks involved, I'd put on a tracksuit and recalled the

Bruce Lee films and *Kung Fu* television series that were highly popular during the 1970s. David Carradine, in particular, striding through the American desert and using various animals and their differing actions as a basis for his deadly moves, stood out in my mind.

After entering the dojo (as the other karate students called it), Enid introduced me to Tim, one of several Black Belts present.

'This is Tom, who works with me, so he needs all the help he can get,' she said.

Tim looked me up and down in an expressionless way. 'Don't worry, there are a few new faces tonight so you'll fit right in,' he assured me.

Enid then set off to another area of the dojo – an area I quite obviously didn't belong in, judging by the high kicks and 'kiai' being yelled by the assorted Black and Brown Belts assembled there.

Quietly spoken, with a tall, lean build and bald head, Tim reminded me of Kwai Chang Caine, the character played by David Carradine in the television series. I was sure my thoughts were shared by the other half-dozen novices around me as Tim manipulated us into a basic stance, and asked us to follow his slow, precise movements. Respect was our overpowering emotion.

I, of course, knew from my time watching Kwai Chang Caine that many martial arts moves are taken from the animal world. So, I found myself not only copying Tim's moves as accurately as I could, but also wondering which animals the moves or sequences could be based on. After twenty minutes, I was really pleased with myself as I held my newly learned 'horseback' stance. I was also sure I was able to sink lower in the stance than the other novices around me, with my right arm held horizontally across my chest, fist clenched tightly, and left hand held open to the side at arm's length. With great pride, I observed my quivering open hand, in the style of a rattlesnake's rattle, which was my understanding of the move. I even noted that the others were so busy working on their 'horseback' stance that their hands were almost motionless, unlike Tim's and mine.

It was then that I saw Enid, who had been keeping a maternal eye on me from across the dojo, walking quickly in my direction. I was sure she was taking a break from her own training to come over and congratulate me on my great progress. The perplexed, even stern look on her face seemed to match her position as a senior Black Belt, an image I'd no doubt have to work on. She indicated, with a gentle and almost hypnotic wave, that I should follow her to a quiet corner – obviously, I thought, so as not to embarrass the others with their comparative weaknesses as she praised me.

'How do you think I'm doing so far?' I asked, with great expectations.

'I forgot to tell you that Tim's got Parkinson's,' she whispered.

So, if Enid was unsure about joining me on the Snowdon trip, I had two options: either bribe her or threaten to accompany her to the karate club again and re-enact my 'rattlesnake stance'.

With Enid signed up, our trip to Snowdon was then

cleared with Gareth. Fortunately, he believed wholeheartedly in outdoor pursuits or activities that build self-esteem and self-confidence. These are, of course, both essential to a young person's development, and are especially true for those students who have special needs.

As usual, I locked up the workshop on Tuesday afternoon as early as possible, so that I could have more time to prepare for the running club. To my great pleasure, I saw Enid with the students making their way to the area of the car park that we claimed as our running club base, weather permitting. Not only had Enid immediately replied, 'Wow, that's a great idea,' to the Snowdon trip, but she'd enthused about it.

By the end of the training session, all of the details were in place and the students were selected – though there was still the need for formal permission to be sought from the appropriate authorities.

After training, Enid and I found a quiet corner of the dining room and went over the details again. We were both happy with the choices of Eve, Priya, Peter and Martin. We'd based our decisions on two things: trust and capability. By trust, we meant that we could trust them to behave well; by capability, we meant that they could cope physically with the challenge. Trust, of course, was by far the most important of these two factors for us.

The dates we chose were Saturday 21st and Sunday 22nd of May, just two weeks away.

My original plan was for a day's walk to the summit, almost certainly ascending the Pyg Track and returning using the Miners' Track. However, Enid's endless enthusiasm and love of adventure had persuaded me to scale the mountain on the Saturday, carrying sleeping bags – along with the added protection of 'bivvy' or waterproof survival bags – and to spend the night on the summit. We'd then come back down the mountain on the Sunday morning.

'When they're older, the only good things some of these children will have will be their memories – so let's make this a brilliant one for them,' she appealed, her bright hazel eyes looking straight into mine.

Put like that, how could I disagree? Hopefully, this memory would include seeing the sunset and sunrise from the summit of Snowdon itself. If all went well, then it truly would be an adventure that the students would remember for a lifetime. As I'd already spent a few nights on the summit myself, before setting off on the Welsh 3000s or simply just spending the night in such a wondrous place under the stars, how could I not agree to Enid's plan?

So, on Saturday, May 21st, with kit contributions collected from several staff members – especially me, Enid and Simon – the six of us were sitting in the minibus ready to set off, having had a special 'mountain lunch' made by the canteen staff, who were all fascinated by the thought of our mini expedition.

As I glanced at Pen-y-Bryn Hostel disappearing in the rear-view mirror of the minibus, I smiled at Enid with one thought on my mind: we were going to make this a special time for the students – after all, they were special students.

It's surprising how the confidence of different students varies when placed in different environments, especially when they're out of their comfort zone. Peter became quieter the further we got from Pen-y-Bryn and the nearer we got to Pen-y-Pass. This was our 'base camp', where we'd park the minibus at the start of our trek up Snowdon.

The reason for Peter's lack of conversation, compared with the others, was that Peter had missed out on the Moel Siabod trip. Following an altercation about biscuits with Alan, he'd been replaced at the last minute by Colin. One thing that Enid and I had made sure to do during our kit check was to ensure that there were no ginger-nut biscuits in any of the rucksacks!

This would be the first time that Peter was away from the urban surroundings he was used to and comfortable in. I knew, as we started our long walk, that the minibus would soon disappear from our sight, along with the tarmac, streetlights and all evidence of towns and villages. Even the familiar sounds of an urban environment, such as traffic or alarms, would be gone. Probably, as soon as Peter had sat down in the minibus, he would have realised that, unlike everyone else around him, he had no experience of what he was about to do. For the first time, he wasn't going to be able to lead the other students. In fact, even his strength and fitness would be of little use when navigating in the dark – which also meant he'd have no idea about the correct pace, or even where he was. He'd need to accept the fact that he was just another one of the followers, a role he wasn't used to or prepared for.

After a photo shoot at Pen-y-Pass car park, which included a final pep talk about safety, kit checks and so on, we set off on our adventure.

'Remember, the first person should always be able to see the last, and the last person should always be able to see the first,' I stressed in my best teacher's voice, as we squeezed through the narrow opening in the wall separating the car park from the start of the Pyg Track.

Although I'd have loved to have had Colin with us, as we set out on the first uneven steps of our journey, I realised it was the right decision not to include him on this occasion. He was still too much of a 'wild card' at times, and Enid and I felt that he didn't have a high enough 'trust' score yet – at least not for this particular adventure. Yorkie and Alan had also been on our radar, but they both had to take second place to Priya and Peter's better physical capabilities. I glanced at my phone: 5:56pm, which gave us three hours and twenty-three minutes to reach the summit. Knowing the fitness levels of this group, I knew we had ample time.

It was a beautiful May evening and we made numerous stops for photographs to be taken. Just after the junction for Crib Goch, we took our longest break as this was the place where Snowdon came into view in all its magnificence. All four students became fixated on the footpath over Crib Goch. Even Peter who had been uncharacteristically quiet up to now wanted to know whether it was as adventurous as it looked. In truth, due to its 'grade 1' scramble along a knife-edge ridge, calling the Crib Goch ridge a footpath is like calling a tiger a domestic cat, but with the right respect it's within most walkers' capability. However, one friend I'd led over it had asked for a photograph to be taken of her as she was literally straddling the ridge, her fearful expression emphasising the sheer drop on either side. With Snowdon and Garnedd Uchaf in the background, it was an excellent composition, clearly showing the exposed and challenging ridge. A few months later, I discovered she'd had it printed in A3 size, framed and hung on the back of her toilet door. Her explanation for this was simple. With emotion in her voice, she'd disclosed, 'If ever I'm constipated, I can take one look at the photo and shit myself again!'

Maybe one day in the future, I'll take some of the students over that ridge, I thought. *And perhaps, some toilet paper in my rucksack might be a good idea!*

Enid and I both kept an eye on the time, as we wanted to reach the summit before nine o'clock, so that we wouldn't miss out on the sunset which, according to the Snowdon summit site, would be at 9:17pm. With time in hand, the Gabion wall defences at the start of the zigzags in the path, which mark the last section on the Pyg Track before joining the Llanberis Path, gave us a favourable place to sit. Here we had something to eat and drink, and looked back at the last section of the route we'd taken. Enid took on the role of tourist guide, pointing out the Clwydian Range in the distance which was now just a light grey silhouette on the far horizon. She then narrated to us one of the legends of Llyn Glaslyn, which translates as 'Lake of the Blue Spring'.

'This is where the Afangc (or Afanc) lives, according to local legend,' Enid explained in her Ynys Môn accent while pointing to the deepest part of the lake. 'You won't see any birds flying over the lake or any fish swimming in it.'

This Afangc, according to legend, had physical characteristics that are akin to many creatures, including a crocodile, dragon and beaver. As '*afanc*' is Welsh for beaver, hypothetically this monster was a survivor from a past age, or a mutation of a large beaver. The story affirms that the Afangc was discovered living in Llyn-yr-Afanc near Betws-y-Coed. It caused the local population endless distress due to the floods it created when it dammed up the river. As all attempts to kill the Afangc failed, it was decided to lure it out of the water by getting a local girl to sing to it. As the Afangc responded so well to her Welsh singing, the villagers then decided it would be bad luck to kill it. Once on dry land, it was quickly captured, chained and moved to Llyn Glaslyn, using a pair of strong oxen to drag it. The steep mountains around Llyn Glaslyn were able to trap it forever. Several places on the route have place names associated with the Afangc's journey, and in the 1930s, Oliver Vaughan, while walking up Snowdon, reported seeing a creature rising to the surface of the lake. The head was pale, or white, and was visible just above the water. Mr Vaughan proclaimed that it wasn't an otter or any other creature with which he was familiar. Could it have been a rare sighting of the Afangc?

With our hot drinks held in cupped hands, and with

various morsels of food in our mouths, we were now all staring down at Llyn Glaslyn, waiting, even wishing, that the still water would be broken by the rising Afangc.

We spent a minute or so concentrating on the waters of the lake, and then having seen no evidence of the Afangc, Enid asked the students:

'What do you know about King Arthur?'

They quickly responded, showing off their knowledge by mentioning the Knights of the Round Table, Merlin, Guinevere and Lancelot.

Peter's pensive manner momentarily brightened up, and he was the one who said, 'You know his sword was called Excalibur,' which was Enid's cue to tell the second legend that was associated with Llyn Glaslyn.

Enid, much to the students' surprise, had a great knowledge of King Arthur. She referred to him as Arthur Pendragon and explained that he was possibly a 5th or 6th-century leader, who'd defended Britain against the Saxons. According to Welsh folklore, Arthur, just before dying, asked Bedivere to throw his sword, Excalibur, into Llyn Glaslyn. Then, once Arthur had died, his knights put his body in a boat to make the trip to Afallon or Avalon as it's called in English. The knights then made their way to a secret cave on the slopes of Y Lliwedd, which Enid pointed out was on the right of the lake. Here the knights would sleep until they were needed again.

Sitting on the Gabion baskets, I looked again for signs of the Afangc but unfortunately none could be seen. Nor could I make out any hollows that might suggest the existence of a medieval cave. As I thought about Enid's rendition of the legend of King Arthur, with her soft Ynys Môn articulation, I was sure of one thing: if King Arthur did exist, then he would have spoken English with a Welsh accent, or even Welsh itself.

Having set off before 6:00pm, we should have reached the standing stone or monolith at the saddle (the low point on the ridge between Snowdon and Carnedd Ugain), which marks the intersection between the Snowdon Ranger and Llanberis Paths, with plenty of time to enjoy the walk to the summit. However, Enid's tales as well as the photographic stops meant that we were a little behind our planned schedule, so I couldn't resist the opportunity for some impromptu training and set everyone off at a jog.

'Does anyone fancy a run?' I asked, knowing it was a rhetorical question.

'To the top?' Eve asked.

'Let's go!' Martin exclaimed.

In the next moment we were all running uphill alongside the railway line as fast as we could.

Once on the summit, after taking far more photographs than needed, we sat ourselves down with a view out to the west. Nine minutes later, as we looked over towards Caernarfon, we were rewarded with the sun setting in breathtaking fashion. The first part of our adventure couldn't have gone better.

Moving away from the summit, to a location just a little below the café, each of us found the most comfortable spot we could. The vending machine just inside the café doors gave a peaceful hum and a dim nightlight for our outdoor 'dorm'. We kept close together for company, safety and reassurance. Snuggled up in our sleeping bags, with an outer bivvy bag for extra protection against the elements, we were all as 'snug as bugs in rugs'. We looked forward to a good night's sleep, especially as it was unusually warm for May. My previous nights under the stars at the top of Snowdon had made me acutely aware of how cold a night on the summit could be, even after there had been a hot summer's day in the valley over nine hundred metres below.

The four students, as well as Enid, had been suitably impressed by the sunset. But even this spectacular scene was now taking second place to the display of stars that shone above us in the unilluminated night sky.

Enid and I had made the decision early on that none of us would sleep inside tents. We were going to make this a real adventure for the students, as well as for us. In these circumstances, we were as comfortable as we could be, as we were 'double-bagged' and had our foam mats underneath us to smooth out the uneven terrain as well as provide an extra layer of insulation. Our heads peeked out into the cooling night air once more, to be amazed again at the display of stars above us, and then we snuggled back into the warmth of our sleeping bags.

Having arranged the supply of sleeping bags and kit for our students attentively, Enid and I had left each other to our own devices as far as our own equipment was concerned. We trusted that our acquired experience and knowledge meant that we'd be able to provide our own paraphernalia adequately.

The six of us were in an area of about five square metres in total, on the paved terrace outside the main entrance to the summit café. Enid and I had stayed on the lower side of the square, as the other three sides had the boundary of a wall or steps, thereby providing some security. Also, from our position, Enid or I would hopefully notice if any of the students were restless during the night or needed to use the 'toilet'.

The students and I had Gore-Tex bivvy bags (or one of the many substitutes for this), which meant that they provided a breathable and waterproof barrier. These would also provide an extra layer of insulation, should the temperature drop unexpectedly. With safety in mind, and to avoid doubling up on equipment, I'd talked through Enid's equipment with her, as she had done with me, but only as a quick checklist; we hadn't gone into any detail.

All seemed well as the chatter and laughter of the students elapsed into silence. With little unnatural light to interfere with the clarity overhead, I took what I thought would be a last look at the Plough constellation, the first formation I'd learned and still one of the few I know. Noting that the North Star was in the right position, I pulled the hood of my sleeping bag over my head, expecting a good night's rest. Then I heard it. Every minute or so, there was a strange rustling sound. The first couple of times it happened, I chose to ignore it. Then it seemed to get louder and lasted for longer. The one consolation I had was that it was far too high above Llyn

Glaslyn for it to be the Afangc looking for a midnight feast.

Whenever I popped my head out of my sleeping bag, there was no evidence of the cause, and no one else seemed to be aware of the unnatural sound. Eventually, with some nervousness, I decided that my only option was to sit up in the cool night air and wait for it to recur. It didn't take long for the rustling to start again. As it did, I noticed that Enid was tossing and turning in her sleep. My first thought was that, although not fully awake, she was also having her sleep disturbed by the unnatural sound echoing around us. Then I realised that there was a direct correlation between Enid's restlessness and the rustling.

Unbeknownst to me, as Enid didn't have her own bivvy bag, she'd borrowed one from Simon at the last minute. He'd pointed out that it was a spare one, which he never used, so she was welcome to have it for the weekend. What he hadn't explained to her was that it was made out of a material that could best be likened to the one used to make crisp packets – in fact, it was polyethylene with a thin outer layer of aluminium.

Every slight movement that Enid made could be compared to fifty hyperactive children crumpling their empty crisp packets in unison. Now that I understood the cause of my sleeplessness, it seemed that even her breathing was creating the rustling effect! To make matters worse, Peter and Martin had developed a severe and loud case of the giggles.

Enid, now awake herself, and nearer to the boys than

I was, asked them, 'What's wrong with you two now?'

Peter, his answer broken by laughing, replied, 'Martin says you borrowed your bivvy bag from a "Walker" called "Smiths".'

I was pleased that Peter was more his normal, light-hearted self again and as I chuckled to myself at his reply, I realised why Simon had been more than happy to lend it to Enid. I made a mental note that all future kit lists must prohibit crisp-packet-style bivvy bags!

I'd set the alarm on my phone for 4:15am, as had Enid. This would give us enough time to quickly gather our kit together and make our way to the summit of Carnedd Ugain, where hopefully we'd be able see the sun rising to the east over the Glyders.

The next morning, Peter appeared to be more reticent again compared to the other students. Even allowing for the early wake-up call, this was unusual. But when Enid chatted to him, he appeared to be full of enthusiasm again, and even said:

'Let me carry the first-aid kit in my rucksack now, cos you carried it up here.'

'Why, thank you, Peter; you're a gentleman,' was her appreciative reply.

Even so, Enid and I were acutely aware of Peter's potential to react badly to a casual comment made by one of the other students. If this did happen, it would cause great challenges for me and Enid, especially as we were isolated on top of the highest mountain in Wales and England. A glance at each other brought reassurance that we were both fully aware of the situation.

I wasn't sure if any of the other students had picked up on Peter's unusual mood, but they all seemed to be giving him a little more space, and respect, than they usually did. To help ensure that Peter stayed in control of himself, Enid took on the role of his 'buddy' as we made our way down the initial stage of the mountain. Soon she'd even, in her quiet reassuring way, got him chatting happily again. It seemed that the more we followed the path alongside the railway line, the more talkative he became. By the time we left the Llanberis Path to make our way to the summit of Carnedd Ugain, Priya was also supporting Enid by taking a turn to chat to Peter.

By 5:00am, we were gathered on Carnedd Ugain's summit waiting for the sunrise. Our early morning wakeup call was rewarded when, a few minutes later, various shades, from dull grey through to varied tones and hues of yellow ochre and bright orange, filled our field of vision. The dark pyramid of Crib Goch was clear to see, as it stood out from the paler Glyders beyond. You could even make out Castell y Gwynt (or 'Castle of the Winds') on the left, as the sun slowly rose over the horizon.

The whole group just stood and absorbed the scene for several minutes before even thinking about trying to take a photograph to capture the all-embracing panorama. Exclamations such as 'Wow', 'Look at the colours' and 'Can we just sit and watch for a bit longer?' rang out from the students. But Peter's contribution will always stay with me:

'Makes all the hard work worth it, doesn't it?'

Enid and I smiled at each other, and I reflected that not only had we given them a special memory but it was one that few others would ever experience.

So, with the sunset and sunrise 'ticked off', it was time to head back to civilization. And it was only when we were close to the final stretch of the Pyg Track that the confident Peter reappeared. He'd talked more and more to Enid throughout the four-hour descent. Enid had done the perfect job. She'd reinforced his abilities as they chatted, building his self-confidence back up throughout the trek down the mountain.

Reaching the minibus, I took off my rucksack and leant it against the wheel of the minibus. I opened the inner zipped pocket to find the safely stored key, taking a moment to look around at the students as I did so. They were gathered by the stone wall at the edge of the car park. Some of them had discarded their rucksacks on the floor and were sitting on the wall. Others still had their rucksacks on, almost willing Enid and I to suggest that we go back up again. It was only now that Peter resumed his usual role, chatting and laughing with the students as they relived their night on Mount Snowdon.

On the descent, I'd deliberately taken extra time, with more breaks than were really necessary. I'd used these breaks to explain some of the mountain skills that were required for adventures like these. These included: planning, weather, navigation, kit choice, fitness, etc. I was particularly pleased with the response from Eve and Priya to these short sessions, as this meant that I was able to imagine them enjoying their own mountain adventures in the future. I even wondered if they might compete in a future mountain marathon together.

As a finale to our weekend, there could be no better place to visit than 'Pete's Eats' in Llanberis. Walking towards either of the entrances, you encounter a bright combination of primary and secondary colours which brighten up the surroundings even on the dullest of Snowdonia days. Sitting around the tables, you'll see some of the fittest and most experienced walkers, climbers and mountain runners you'll ever come across. All are fully aware of the charms of 'Pete's Eats', with its appropriate selection of food and drink chalked up on the large blackboards above their heads.

I always found that this was a great place to visit and would often come across old friends here, while they, or I, were enjoying a well-deserved pint of tea. And it was here that I discovered Enid's Achilles heel. With Pen-y-Bryn covering the cost of the breakfast, Enid had decided to treat everyone to a drink of their choice.

'*Diolch am amser wych* – thank you for a great time,' she announced, before asking each of us which special drink we'd like.

An assortment of teas, coffees and hot chocolates were requested, and she walked to the bar to place the order. The two young girls behind the counter were chatting away in Welsh with Enid – probably about fashion, as all three seemed to be more dressed up than was necessary for this particular location. Enid, even after a night of sleeping out on a mountaintop, and in her outdoor gear, looked like she was on her way to an outdoor-adventure magazine photo shoot. The two girls serving her, like Enid, drew admiring glances from the increasing number of male customers who were filling up the café. Both the young girls had obviously taken great care over their makeup, especially their drawn-on eyebrows! But I couldn't help thinking that, even though they were wearing aprons, the lack of material used to make up the rest of their clothing wouldn't be fully in keeping with today's health and safety guidelines.

Then there was an unexpected silence from the trio. Seeing them motionless as well as speechless, I wondered whether I should go over and help. Enid was standing with her bank card in her hand, obviously confused. She'd taken the machine off the counter and when 'contactless' hadn't worked, she'd tried repeatedly to insert her card to pay. It was now that the taller of the two girls, having spoken only in Welsh till now, advised Enid in English:

'That's my calculator!'

It seems that Enid wears contact lenses because she's near-sighted. Having spent the night on Snowdon, in the morning she'd decided not to put them back in, relying on her long vision for the walk down the mountain.

On the drive back, I made a point of putting words like 'payment', 'card', 'machine', 'vision' and so on into our conversation with the students whenever I could, knowing that only Enid would realise that I was pursuing the funny side of her morning predicament. However, when she became unusually quiet, I considered her 2nd Dan Black Belt and started talking about the weather!

Chapter Twelve
The Perfect Training Ground

Everyone thought that the night out on Snowdon's summit had been a great success. What Enid and I were particularly pleased about was just how keen all the students were to spend more time out and about in the mountains, especially in the Snowdonia area and especially with us.

For once, the timing of the students' enthusiasm couldn't have been better. The months of June and July meant that we had longer hours of daylight and, hopefully, warmer and dryer weather. I was looking forward to a stronger bond being established between the students and the staff. Altogether, I imagined that I was going to be part of a wonderful experience.

The running club had now progressed to having extra training sessions on the Clwydian Hills, as an activity option when I was working in the hostel. I was so pleased at how popular this activity was with some of the students and it made my Sunday shift so enjoyable. Two routes, similar in content, were always popular with the students. Each week I'd divide those who turned up into two groups – three if you included Eve, who always ran greater distances than any of the others. The weaker runners would set off first, at a walking pace, only starting their run when the initial steep ascent was out of the way. The stronger ones, depending on their abilities, would follow the same route but at a set time later, hopefully allowing everyone to finish together. It also meant that hostel staff helpers, who weren't runners themselves, could take part in, and enjoy, the activity.

One characteristic of the running club that I was really pleased about was the growing empathy that the members of each team felt for each other. Support, such as 'Come on, keep going', 'You can do it', 'It's not far now' and 'You're getting better all the time', was being voiced by the stronger runners so often that I hardly had to contribute myself. No one was ever left feeling deflated because they'd been left to finish by themselves. Considering the nature of some of the students, this was probably more significant than their running achievements!

Moel Arthur lay in the middle of the two routes. The first route was about nine kilometres long, with two hundred and seven metres of height gain. It started at the car park between Pen y Cloddiau and Moel Arthur. This took the direct path over the top of Pen y Cloddiau to the minor road beyond. Turning left onto the road, a circular route would lead you back to the woods below the starting point. A good uphill track then took you back to the starting point. A great bonus of this route is the spectacular scenery in all directions on the higher sections, which you can admire as you're running along. On a clear day, you can see Snowdon to the west-south-west and Blackpool Tower to the north-north-east.

The second route was a great favourite of mine. Compared with the first, it was about a kilometre shorter, with about eighty-five metres less of height gain. This time, you'd start at the car park at the south-east side of Moel Arthur. A precipitous ascent took you to the west of Moel Llys-y-Coed. From here, you continued along the Offa's Dyke Path, past Moel Drwyll, to the summit of Moel Famau. At times the conditions underfoot on this route were as near perfect as you could get. The malleable peat underfoot was as comfortable as any synthetic running track; it was almost like running on air. Although various circular routes were possible, I always got the students to return the same way. A midway stop at the Jubilee Tower for a chocolate bar and a cool drink was always a welcome and well-deserved treat for the students. They also enjoyed the admiration they received from the walkers who'd come up from one of the shorter footpaths on the north-west side of the Clwydians.

Along with our Tuesday training, my plan was to have a trip to Snowdonia every other weekend in June, weather permitting. Each time, we'd use a combination of walking and running during the outing. I decided to take the easy option of using the routes, or a variation of them, that I'd used for my own mountain marathon training. With my own times locked into my memory

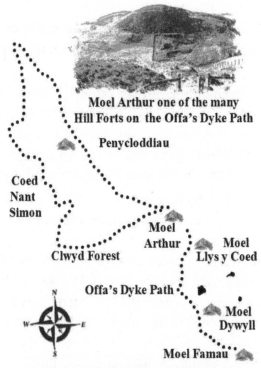

Moel Arthur one of the many Hill Forts on the Offa's Dyke Path

Penycloddiau

Coed
Nant
Simon

Moel
Arthur

Moel
Llys y Coed

Clwyd Forest

Offa's Dyke Path

Moel
Dywyll

Moel Famau

Routes 6 & 7: Route 6 from Car Park below
Moel Llys y Coed to Moel Famau and return:
Approximately 9 kilometres with
207 metres' height gain.
Route 7 from west side of Moel Arthur go
anticlockwise around Penycloddiau;
Approximately 8 kilometres with
122 metres' height gain.

banks, I quickly became aware of how competent many of the students were. However, even when compared to those in the stronger group, Eve's performances stood out.

She really is in a class of her own, I thought to myself. In simple terms, she never seemed to get tired or out of breath.

It had been during our last outing in May – the 29th, in fact – while sitting on the summit of Tryfan, that I'd decided to tell the students the story of Josh Naylor and his famous Welsh 3000s run in 1973. I first read about the Welsh 3000s in Thomas Firbank's book *I Bought a Mountain*[10]. The book contains a detailed account of his traverse of the Welsh 3000s, which Thomas and his wife Esmè had made. As the route we were tackling that day was traditionally the second stage of the Welsh 3000s, it seemed more than appropriate to relate the tale.

It was a relaxed reunion, following our adventure the previous weekend, of the 'Snowdon Six': myself, Enid, Eve, Priya, Peter and Martin. Even Eve couldn't visualise the necessary minimum distance of fifty-nine kilometres, with a minimum height gain of four thousand metres, being achieved in only four hours and forty-six minutes.

I then explained that the current record for men is even less: four hours and nineteen minutes, achieved by Colin Donnelly[11] in 1989. The current women's record, made in 1989 by Angela Carson[12], is just as impressive: five hours and twenty-eight minutes. You also have to bear in mind, though, that it was Josh's first visit to Wales when he achieved his time. He had no pacemakers; no one would have kept up with him at the time anyway! Also, the paths have greatly improved since then, due to the efforts of the Snowdonia National Park team as well as the ever-increasing numbers of walkers using them.

With only the last, third stage of the Welsh 3000s not attempted by any of them, the students were enthusiastic to see just what it involved. Especially as, from our vantage point beside Adam and Eve, we were looking across at the profile of the initial part of the third stage – the steep scramble up to the top of Pen yr Ole Wen. This led you straight onto the Carneddau Mountain Range. The plan was made, there and then, to tackle the eight mountaintops on the Carneddau as soon as possible. We'd start at Ogwen Cottage, with Pen yr Ole Wen being our first summit, and finish with Foel Fras. Many walkers consider that this route takes a full day's walking in itself, let alone being a finale to the Welsh 3000s. I decided not to tell the students then that we'd have to go to the top of another mountain, Drum, a mere seven hundred and eighty metres high, before we could get back to the minibus. We'd finish, finally, at the Bwlch y Ddeufaen car park, to the west of Rowen.

Before we set off from the summit of Tryfan that day, all but Priya took the required leap from Adam to Eve. She was all set to do it, having been psyched up by Eve, who'd already soaked up the adrenaline rush, but unfortunately, just as Priya was going to take her turn, one of the other walkers who was out for the day misjudged the distance or his ability. This resulted in him

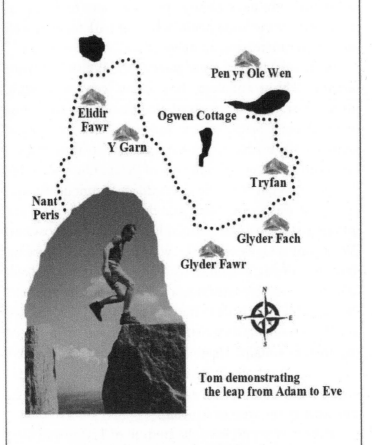

Pen yr Ole Wen

Ogwen Cottage

Elidir Fawr

Y Garn

Nant Peris

Tryfan

Glyder Fach

Glyder Fawr

Tom demonstrating
the leap from Adam to Eve

Route 8: Second stage of the Welsh 3000s:
Approximately 16 kilometres
with 1,417 metres' height gain.

crashing spectacularly into the smaller monolith 'Eve', just as Priya was about to climb onto 'Adam'. No doubt this played its part in Priya's decision to postpone the leap until another day. The amount of skin he was capable of removing from one of his shins in this one action was astonishing! It seemed to be matched only by the amount of blood he was losing. Not only did Priya decline to make the leap, but during the time it took for us to gather our things together, no one else took the opportunity to 'gain the freedom of Tryfan' either.

A week later, and the six of us were sitting having lunch on top of the highest summit of the Carneddau Range – Carnedd Llewelyn, one thousand and sixty-four metres above sea level, and the second highest mountain in Wales. As well as getting the strenuous height gain from Ogwen Cottage to Pen yr Ole Wen out of the way, we'd bagged Carnedd Dafydd and Yr Elen. So, by comparison, the remainder of the day's walk, over the rolling summits of the Carneddau to the Bwlch y Ddeufaen car park, seemed easy.

I'd used a well-known technique to even out the pace of the group. This had been explained to me by Arnold, an old friend of mine from my days at Ridall, who taught Outdoor Pursuits. First of all, you need good knowledge of the individual group members. Then, at the appropriate time, you select the slowest and get this person to navigate for the whole group. As if by magic, once the map and compass are in their hands, 'navigator's disease' takes over. It's as if a fast-forward button has been pressed.

With a little input to occupy the faster members, easily achieved by giving them 'photograph duty' or taking time to describe interesting points along the way, the whole group moves on at a far more even pace.

As we were about to set off on the final leg, Martin, now well rested and with renewed energy after his packed lunch, complete with Mars bar, stood up.

'Why don't we run for a bit? It's perfect for training up here,' he suggested, with a smile on his face.

'Is that OK, Tom?' Eve quickly enthused. 'It's not that far now, is it?'

Everyone was looking at me in anticipation of my answer.

'I suppose we could, but only if you really want to...' I teased.

So, with perfect weather and a clear path to follow, Martin set off, proudly leading the way.

As it was just under five kilometres to reach Foel Fras from Carnedd Llewelyn, the pace was a fast one. As the students arrived at the final slope up to Foel Fras, Martin and Peter made a sprint to try to achieve second place. They'd both accepted, only two hundred metres after leaving Carnedd Llewelyn, that Eve, although not the first to set off, was going to be the first to reach the summit of Foel Fras. A wise decision by the pair, as Eve finished the run about nine minutes ahead of them, according to her watch.

Standing on the summit of Foel Fras, we enjoyed taking in the fresh mountain air. We were all pleased with the day's achievements. Then, with what seemed like a telepathic connection, a group decision was made. Completing the Welsh 3000s was no longer going to be something that others had achieved; it was going to be something that we'd all do in the future. In fact, full of the day's success, it was going to be in the very near future!

Two thoughts filled my mind as I drove us back to Pen-y-Bryn. The first was a mixture of all the complexities that would be involved in tackling the Welsh 3000s with a group from Pen-y-Bryn Hostel. The second was of Eve being nearly ten minutes ahead of Martin and Peter when she'd reached Foel Fras. This meant that on a mountain run of about five kilometres and seventy-six metres in height gain, her pace was about two minutes per kilometre faster than theirs.

Previous Tuesday training sessions had shown me just how competitive Martin could be. Often Martin and I had finished the last section on a Tuesday together. He'd always put everything into beating me, which he always did. On these occasions, Eve ran by herself. I hadn't recorded any of her times for several months. I now realised that this was something I had to do at the earliest opportunity.

As we'd pulled up outside the hostel, I could see that Little Dave's 1994 burgundy Mini Cooper was parked there. Not the car you'd associate with a person of Little Dave's stature, but as he'd explained to me, it was one of the few cars that he could sit in comfortably. However, this was a bit disconcerting for other road users as, when he'd got the seat adjusted back to his required position,

209

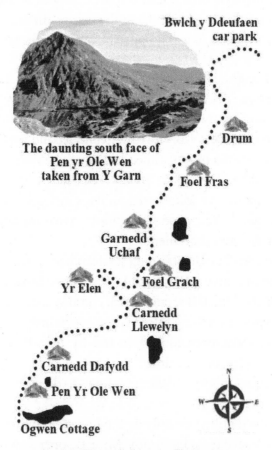

Bwlch y Ddeufaen
car park

Drum

Foel Fras

The daunting south face of
Pen yr Ole Wen
taken from Y Garn

Garnedd
Uchaf

Foel Grach

Yr Elen

Carnedd
Llewelyn

Carnedd Dafydd

Pen Yr Ole Wen

Ogwen Cottage

Route 9: Third Stage of the Welsh 3000s:
Approximately 18.5 kilometres
with 1,027 metres' height gain.

it looked as if he was sitting in the back, with an invisible man chauffeuring him around. Interestingly, although Little Dave loved his Mini, he wasn't keen to replace it with a new one. It seems, although the outside of the new model is a lot larger, the front seats, even when pushed fully back, don't give as much leg room as his classic model.

Everyone on the minibus knew that Little Dave wasn't supposed to be working this weekend, so as soon as the students saw his Mini, their conversation changed.

'Little Dave's here!'

'What's happened now?'

'Who's kicked off?'

We all guessed that while we'd been having a great day out, something serious had happened back at the hostel. It was as if a drug had entered the air conditioning of the minibus. All four of the students were immediately 'high', and if not for Enid's intervention, the boys would have leapt out of the minibus before it had stopped moving. Though, to be fair, although we weren't showing it, Enid and I were just as keen to know 'What's occurring?' as Colin would have put it.

Eve, Priya, Peter and Martin were inside Pen-y-Bryn before Enid and I had even got out of the bus. Dianne (no longer considered a new member of staff as she'd acclimatised so well to her role in the hostel) and Helen were just inside the main entrance, apparently on guard duty.

'Bethan's kicked off, good style,' Helen explained. 'She's thrown tables and chairs all over the place so now there are pieces everywhere and she's managed to smash three windows.'

'Bryn won't be pleased when he sees the mess in the morning,' Dianne added, 'he'd only just replaced another pane that Bethan broke before he went home!'

'I tried to stop her running past me in the corridor, then I heard all the noise from the dining room.' Helen shook her head and sighed.

'These things happen here. Don't worry about it, Helen,' Enid said, placing a hand on Helen's shoulder. Then she paused and took a deep breath. 'You two wait here; Tom and I will go and lend a hand clearing up, won't we, Tom?'

'No problem,' I replied. 'Like Enid says, it's just one of those things that makes working here so different.'

It seemed, unbeknownst to everyone, that Bethan had taken a romantic fancy to Colin. A match certainly not made in heaven! The problem was, though, that Colin only had eyes for the most beautiful women in the world, and I do mean the world – think movie stars, models and celebrities.

So, after Bethan had spent a considerable amount of time plucking up the courage to ask Colin, 'Will you go out with me?', Colin in his own diplomatic and unique way, had replied, 'Fuck off, you silly bitch.'

This was brave of Colin, to say the least. It wasn't so much like lighting a fuse; it was more like pressing a nuclear button.

Fortunately, Bethan, in all her 'kick-offs', had never hurt anyone, except sometimes herself. But property –

tables, chairs, bins, etc., – was another thing. Her speciality, of course, was glass, especially windows. Entering the dining room, the damage was clear to see. One large window, four panes in all, still had the wooden chair stuck in it which was hanging from the wooden cross members of the frame. Bizarrely, my first thought was that the image would be comparable to a piece of art created by Tracy Emin.

The clinking of the glass that Tony, one of the hostel staff, was brushing up from the window on the opposite side of the room focused my attention over there. Just one broken pane in this case, as Bethan had used her fist to smash it as she ran past.

Pausing momentarily, Tony looked at Enid and me in dismay. 'There's another window gone in *Berwyn's* corridor.'

Enid and I were both tired and ready to go home. The day had been physically tiring and although we'd had no problems, teachers never really relax when taking students out for the day. Peter and Martin had gone to their rooms, probably to get first-hand information from Alan or Roy. Eve and Priya, for the time being, couldn't go down the corridor leading to their rooms in *Berwyn* because of the broken glass scattered throughout it.

Although all of those on duty were capable staff, Little Dave knew all too well the effect an incident like this could have on morale. This is why he'd asked Dianne and Helen to stay at the main entrance. He knew they needed to get some fresh air or have some time out.

Apart from those who'd been out for the day with

Enid and me, all other students, aside from Joe, had gone to their rooms. So, for the time being at least, managing the students was no problem. Simon was with Colin, making sure he didn't set anyone else off. Little Dave was with Bethan, doing the required counselling. This left Tony, with some help from Joe, to do all the clearing up. Not able to go to their own rooms, and without being asked, Eve had found some additional dustpans and brushes from the store cupboard. Within a minute or so, she was helping Tony clear up the remaining glass from the dining room floor. Meanwhile Priya had filled the kettle and switched it on.

'Would anyone like a cuppa?' she asked as she came back into the dining room. She knew this would be a welcomed question.

How could Enid and I leave and go home at a time like this? It was going to be a longer day than we'd imagined.

With everything safely tidied up, we sat down for our second cuppa a little after 10:30pm – one and a half hours later than I thought I'd be setting off home. Tony had asked Joe to help us move the heavier furniture back into place. I wondered how Bethan had managed to move some of the tables so far from their original position by herself. I looked around fondly at the others present, enjoying their hot drinks with toast, at Joe's request. Staff and students had worked together, as a team, to calm the storm and clear up the debris.

Joe took this opportunity to point out the obvious –

something that everyone working in similar establishments knows.

'It's a full moon. These kinds of things always happen on a full moon. You should get extra staff in once a month,' he said to Little Dave, who'd now left Bethan alone to consider her actions.

I could see Dianne and Helen nodding in agreement.

'The four staff on duty handled the situation as well as it could be handled,' Little Dave replied, which was code for 'there's not enough money'!

'How's Annie?' Joe asked Little Dave in reply, his sense of humour having kicked in.

This led to a confused look from everyone, including Eve, who's usually on the same wavelength as Joe.

'What are you on about now?' Eve asked.

I could only think of *Little Orphan Annie* and *Annie Get Your Gun*, and neither quite made sense. He laughed and, after a few seconds, started singing quietly the opening lines of 'Walking on Broken Glass'[13] by Annie Lennox. Immediately, it made complete sense and we all burst out laughing.

Unfortunately, there was little that could be done to avoid interaction between the students, and that could lead to relationship problems; after all, we're talking about teenagers, many of whom had complicated emotional backgrounds. But it's not just when students fall out that incidents happen.

When working at Ridall, I'd opted out of joining a school ski experience to Borovets in Bulgaria. I use the word 'experience' rather than 'holiday', as I've been on several of these 'experiences' before. On this one, two of the students had become too friendly. The staff had taken fifteen students with them and brought sixteen back – well, maybe fifteen and a bit! Two of the sixteen year-olds had decided to really enjoy each other's company, and just over eight months later, a beautiful baby girl was born!

Even after such a perfect day and knowing that I wouldn't have to complete any paperwork about Bethan's incident, while driving home, it wasn't the lyrics of Lou Reed's 'Perfect Day'[14] but those of 'Walking on Broken Glass', courtesy of Joe, that I was singing to myself.

Six hours at home and I'd be going back for the start of another day at Ysgol Abaty. Such a pleasant thought to send me to sleep!

Chapter Thirteen
Traversing The Welsh 3000s

By the end of the training session on 7th June, Enid and I had set a date for the Welsh 3000s: Saturday 25th June. It was just under two weeks away, but we were all 'hill fit' already and it was nearing the day with the longest amount of daylight: June 21st. We'd also decided, after much discussion, to increase the number of our party of adventurers to eight. The seventh would be Simon, even though it had been Simon, or rather his bivvy bag, that had been responsible for my lack of sleep on Snowdon's summit a few weeks earlier.

Simon's knowledge and experience would reduce the leadership pressure on me greatly, allowing for a more relaxed atmosphere. The final member, and a surprising one at that, would be Colin. Colin had taken to walking and scrambling like a duck to water. This should, of course, have been obvious to me seeing as my first encounter with him was when he was on the school roof. Even his hairstyle seemed to say 'outdoor adventurer' when I looked at him now. More importantly, since the start of the year, he'd matured and had no incidents recorded on his file lately. He'd also attended every training session of the running club, come rain or shine, and there had been a lot of rain!

The more experience we could have of the route the better, before the full length of the 3000s was attempted. Up to now, if you divided the Welsh 3000s route into three stages, with the exception of Colin, we'd all completed the third stage: Ogwen Cottage to Foel Fras. Simon, like me, hadn't just completed the 3000s many times before, he'd also enjoyed leading parties of walkers over them.

The first-stage practice – Snowdon to Nant Peris – was scheduled for the following Tuesday evening to fit in with existing staff commitments. Although it was to be a week later, the excellent forecast seemed fairly reliable due to the lingering high pressure.

Enid was going to be off work on that day, and Simon changed his late shift to an early one, with Little Dave's approval. This suited me perfectly, as I still needed to get a current record of Eve's running ability.

My plan was simple: we'd drop Eve off at Llanberis, from where she could run the eight kilometres uphill to Pen y Pass. We'd wait for her there, having taken the easier option of using the minibus! This might also give us a more even playing field as we later made our way along the Pyg Track to the summit of Snowdon trying to keep up with her. Once at the summit, we'd make the easy trek to Garnedd Ugain and then the far more difficult one to Crib Goch.

I thought back to that day in May, on our way up Snowdon, when the students had looked with trepidation at the sheer ridge and wondered if it would be adventurous or simply terrifying to cross it. Now, with the methodical training we'd completed, I knew their mountain capability well and was confident they'd all take it in their stride.

Finally, we'd use the north ridge of Crib Goch to access the valley near Llyn Glas, which would lead us down to the Llanberis Pass and onto Nant Peris. After a time check there, we could have a leisurely walk along the road to our minibus in Llanberis.

'See you soon!' I shouted and gave Eve a thumbs up. Then, remembering to start the stopwatch on my phone, we set off up the winding Llanberis Pass in the minibus.

'See you in a bit,' was her upbeat reply as she waved us off.

As is my nature (belt and braces), I'd also noted the time: 4:27pm. Knowing that it would be a little under five hours before it got dark, the hope was that we'd be off the higher ground well before dusk.

I easily found a parking spot in the Pen y Pass car park. Toilet stops were quickly taken, before a visit to the café to stock up on 'energy sources'. Mars bars, as always, were the favoured choice of everyone.

'Have you got your Mars bar?' I asked Martin as the group exited the shop.

'I've got two, cos it's a special occasion,' he answered

with a smirk on his face, as he held up the chocolate bars to confirm his statement.

Footwear changed and rucksacks on, we gathered together to await Eve's arrival.

'Here she comes now!' Priya, who'd placed herself at the entrance to the car park, shouted cheerily. And she was right, Eve was running towards us far sooner than I would have thought possible!

I grabbed my phone and looked at the miniscule time indicator above the larger rapidly changing stopwatch function. Squinting my eyes more than I would have liked, I made out the time 4:59 before it changed to 5:00. I reached the entrance of the car park at the same time as Eve came through it. A quick press of my thumb and I had an accurate time for Eve's run. Not only that, but I could cross-reference it against other elite runners' times as they'd set off on the first part of the Snowdon Marathon.

Now, as I've mentioned before, I have a lot of statistics stored in my head, such as Josh Naylor's time for his 1973 Welsh 3000s run: four hours, forty-six minutes. Although the record for this first part of the Snowdon Marathon wasn't one of my memorised facts, I knew immediately that Eve's time was impressive. The stopwatch on my phone displayed 33:46, but just how impressive this was I'd have to check later.

The walk up the Pyg Track to Snowdon's summit was quickly achieved, though it would have been even faster if the students had had their way, as they frequently asked, 'Can we run this bit now, Tom?' And although it seemed like a good idea to them at the time, I knew we would all have regretted it later.

After ascending to Snowdon's summit, we'd jogged down to Carnedd Ugain and then carefully made our way towards the Crib Goch path. As we traversed carefully over the Crib y Ddysgl ridge, the students were pleasantly surprised at how conveniently placed and secure the handholds were, just as I'd said they would be. Once on the more exposed Crib Goch ridge, they moved at a sensible pace, which is always recommended here, not only because of the safety issues which have to be considered due to the feeling of exposure, but also because of its location which provides stunning views of the surrounding mountains.

All of us stopped occasionally to take in the scene around us, or to allow other walkers going in the opposite direction to pass by safely. Everyone, including Peter, who was now completely at home in a mountain environment, chatted and joked as they made their way carefully over the ridge, even pausing to take each other's photographs. I marvelled at how far they had come as mountaineers, and at their increased self-confidence.

However, the North Ridge exit from Crib Goch, with its awful loose scree, isn't one of my favourite routes and this was the only time that any of the students complained.

As Peter so well expressed it, 'This is rubbish isn't it.'

Once onto the road, everyone's spirits lifted once more as we made the easy run down to Nant Peris. Later, as we sat alongside the minibus, tucking into well-earned fish and chips, we were each able to reflect on the day. Everything had gone well, and everyone had their favourite part to retell. Only one bit of my plan had been unsuccessful; Eve's initial eight kilometres seemed to have had no effect on her pace at all when she'd joined up with us again.

I noted that four hours and forty-eight minutes after setting off up the Pyg Track, we were back in Llanberis.

The drive back to Pen-y-Bryn was almost silent. Spending the evening walking, running and of course eating had, at the time, seemed easily within our capabilities. However, with 12th June set for the second practice stage, and with all the fish and chips finished, the day's exertions were now taking their effect. The journey back was being used by all, but me, to nap.

With no concerns about the day occupying my thoughts, I found my mind wandering back to Eve's initial run of the day, and her time of thirty-three minutes and forty-six seconds. I know that many runners will consider a time of over thirty minutes for an eight-kilometre run to be nothing special. But these eight kilometres were run simply for enjoyment and without any pressure of competition. They also included a height gain of about two hundred and ninety metres!

Sunday the 12th arrived and the eight of us were assembled again, ready to take on the middle section of the Welsh 3000s. The weather on this occasion couldn't have been more foreboding. Yet, in another way, it couldn't have been better. With grey clouds overhead,

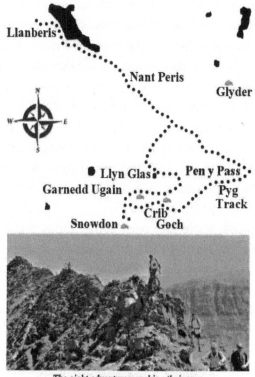

The eight adventurers making their way
over Crib Goch.

Route 10: First stage of the Welsh 3000s:
Approximately 13 kilometres with 913 metres'
height gain, plus Eve's initial run from
Llanberis to Pen y Pass, an additional
8 kilometres with 290 metres' height gain.

and light rain swirling around us, not one person had a smile on their face as we crossed the car park from the hostel to the minibus.

Good fortune had been with us on all our previous walks and this had resulted in the students thinking that the risk of getting lost in the mist on a mountain was an urban myth. This also applied to the day out we'd had in the same area just a fortnight previously. I would have preferred the comfort of better weather for myself; however, the mist that I expected to be covering the higher levels of the Glyders would give the students a real taste of the dangers that a mountain walk can offer, if not fully prepared. This would provide them with a real and true respect for the mountains.

Although there had been some humorous banter on the drive to Nant Peris, this quickly disappeared on arrival at the car park. This was the first time, on a mountain day out, that none of the students rushed to get out of the minibus. The air temperature was a cool ten degrees celsius with a light drizzle being carried on the breeze. The inability to see anything above one hundred and fifty metres made the environment appear ominous.

For the first time, waterproof trousers were being pulled on as well as hats and gloves. We had five peaks to summit, and I was especially glad I had Simon with me; I'd experienced walking on the Glyders in thick mist before and welcomed the opportunity to share the navigation with him, if necessary.

Seeing the lack of enthusiasm on the students' faces, Simon joyfully enthused, 'The sooner we get started, the sooner we get finished.'

Colin tightened the belt on his rucksack and, with a grin on his face, said, 'Come on, you lot, let's get going then.'

Having set off at 10:00am, we were still seeing little but each other forty minutes later. Occasionally, as we crossed the high ridge, features such as Castell y Gwynt appeared briefly before becoming invisible again. The first time a reasonable view appeared was as we reached the halfway point between Castell y Gwynt and Glyder Fach.

'Let's have a break here, Tom, while we can actually see something!' Simon suggested, realising that our visibility might be reduced further at any time.

'I think that's a really good idea,' I replied, noting the relief on the faces of the rest of the group.

Large rocks provided seats for each of us as we delved into our rucksacks for our well-earned refreshments. Surveying the vista as we tucked into our 'elevenses', the tops of Elidir Fawr, Y Garn and the higher Caerneddau peaks materialised like enchanted islands rising up from an eerie sea. Then just as we were all setting off, the brume rose again, swallowing up the peaks once more. Even the Cantilever Stone, usually a distinctive feature on the high ridge, was passed with no evidence of its existence.

Poor visibility had greatly slowed our pace. Simon and I had also taken time to explain, and demonstrate, how to use a map and compass to navigate, even when there was little visibility. With the weather deteriorating all the time, rather than complete the last summit, Tryfan,

Simon and I agreed to head straight from the saddle near the lower end of Bristly Ridge to Ogwen Cottage, thus avoiding Tryfan altogether. Little Dave had agreed to move our minibus, with Imre H's assistance, from the car park at Pen y Pass to Ogwen Cottage at some point during the day so that it would be there for our arrival. Colin was the only one not to have summited Tryfan and he was downhearted by this change of plan; he was desperately keen to gain 'the freedom of Tryfan' by making the leap from Adam to Eve.

'There's too much mist today, Colin, and you wouldn't be able to make the leap in this swirling wind anyway,' Simon explained. 'So even if we went to the top of Tryfan, we wouldn't allow anyone to jump; it's far too dangerous.'

Colin was then more than happy to return to the minibus and to get out of the dismal weather as soon as possible.

Over seven hours after setting off, we saw the minibus parked up, waiting for us. I think this was the first time in the whole day that we all smiled together. All the students now appreciated how the weather, and in particular mist and fog, could make a mountain far more dangerous than in fine conditions. They also had a greater respect for the staff who'd guided them and kept them safe for several hours through the gloomy mountains.

My running club on the 19th took an unusual turn. There were so many students that wanted to take part in Sunday training that it would have been unsafe to follow the usual format of two or three groups setting off at different times, as an average pace would never have been maintained. I'm glad to say that Simon came to my rescue. The number of students remaining in the hostel over the weekend meant that he was able to join me and Alice (who was covering Enid's shift as a favour), making supervision much more manageable.

'Why don't we use Pen y Ball Hill as our training circuit?' Simon suggested. 'Then we could—'

'—You carry on,' I interrupted as he started to explain what he had in mind. 'I know whatever you're thinking will be great!'

Simon sent Colin and Peter off to the storeroom to collect the cones that were used as markers for football matches. As soon as they got back, we all set off in one large group. A slow jog, as our warm-up, took us towards the top of Pen y Ball. Once there, Simon insisted that we should avoid the impact of the steepness of the hill by walking down it. Colin and Peter were then instructed to place the cones at the side of the road every so often as we descended. Even so, we seemed to reach the bottom of the hill in no time at all.

The exercise that Simon had devised was simple, but productive. Each student set off from the lowest cone and ran to the two cones that Simon had placed at the top of the hill. Then they'd make their way back down to the penultimate cone from the bottom one. Once there, you'd turn around and run back up to the top. This was repeated, but each time you'd only go down as far as the cone before the previous one. In all, Simon had divided

Pen y Ball Hill into six sections.

The slower and more inexperienced runners only managed the first circuit, running up and down the hill once, if that. After all, it was extremely steep. This wasn't a problem as they were able to collect the cones that were no longer needed on their slow walk back to the top. Simon always made sure he was lower on the hill than anyone else. From there, he could gauge how individual students were coping, adjusting their required sections appropriately. This resulted not only in most of the students finishing within a few minutes of each other, but, for once, Alice and I were able to enjoy a casual walk with time to chat.

Once we'd passed the fourth pair of cones, Simon asked Alice to make her way to the top of the hill. This meant that she should get there ahead of the first student to finish, and she could supervise the runners as well as applaud them as they reached the last two cones.

When Simon and I eventually reached the top of the hill, we saw the students gathered around Alice, all in suitable states of breathlessness and exhaustion. Even Eve, who'd completed the first longer section twice, looked unusually jaded.

Alice asked me to praise Roy specifically, who'd managed to keep pace with Martin and Peter – though he'd been given permission by Simon to rest for one of their sections. I was really pleased about Roy's success as I'd always thought he was a natural athlete. Though Roy wasn't usually competitive, he'd obviously been spurred on by this type of training session. When I mentioned how pleased I was with his performance, he reckoned that it was Alice's fault. Apparently, she'd given them a lesson on the benefits of having a 'square meal' every day. (This was originally a nautical term as sailors used square, wooden plates, but now it refers to a balanced diet.)

He explained, 'After Alice's lesson, I've only gone and eaten toast, waffles, cream crackers and ravioli pasta.' Then, unable to control it any longer, a cheeky grin spread across his face.

I didn't know what I was most impressed by, his sense of humour or his knowledge of square-shaped pasta!

The morning of the Welsh 3000s had arrived. At 2:00am on Saturday the 25th of June, Pen-y-Bryn Hostel looked dead to the world as I parked my car.

Colin came running out to meet me, shouting, 'I've made your cup of tea; it's in the dining room.'

Everyone, except Enid, was there waiting for me, and after a few sips from my cup, I helped to carry the remaining gear to the minibus. Then, just as the last rucksack was being loaded, the roar of a motorbike became louder as Enid pulled up alongside the minibus on her Harley Davidson.

'Sorry I'm late; traffic was bad,' she joked.

Seven minutes later and we were heading through Pantasaph and the adventure had started.

Not surprisingly, only two cars were occupying the Pen y Pass car park when we arrived. After parking as near as possible to the start of the Pyg Track, and with a 'before the Welsh 3000s picture' taken, we were soon heading towards the summit of Snowdon. It was now 2:50am and, unlike our last walk up Snowdon, there would be no time for extended photo shoots, engaging stories or leisurely refreshment stops. Wanting to complete the 3000s within the possible seventeen hours of daylight, there was going to be little time for dilly-dallying.

With perfect timing, we reached Snowdon's summit in the early morning daylight.

'Wow, where did they come from?' was Colin's surprised reaction on discovering four men and one woman running up the final stretch of the mountain, alongside the railway line, to arrive at the summit with us.

Apparently, Snowdon was their third mountaintop of the day as they'd already summited Crib Goch and Garnedd Ugain, which is my preferred choice of route for the Welsh 3000s Challenge. However, Simon and I had agreed that reaching the summit of Crib Goch as the sun rose was a higher risk than reaching the top of Snowdon as our first summit. With Crib Goch as our third peak, we'd use the North Ridge of it to make our way down to the road below, as we'd done on our practice. By the time we'd taken our compulsory photo on the summit of Snowdon as evidence, the five runners had already disappeared down the Llanberis Path.

With a recorded start time of 4:48am, we set off for the second summit. I'd managed to convince all of the students that this was to be an enjoyable day. Although time was of the essence, the challenge needed to be done at a realistic pace, with appropriate short stops for photographs and views along the way. I didn't consider these stops to be 'dilly-dallying' as they'd also serve as disguised opportunities for everyone to have a physical rest without realising this was the case. Little Dave had agreed to meet us at three locations. This would reduce the need to carry additional and much-needed refreshments. It would also be an opportunity to retire from the task if anyone felt it was necessary. The first of these locations was Nant Peris. So, in less than two hours' time, we'd be able to tuck into a hearty meal and have a hot drink out of the stainless-steel flasks that had generously been bought by Pen-y-Bryn for this very occasion.

The lack of people on the Crib Goch ridge and traffic on the road down to Nant Peris were a great relief to me and Simon as we were both well aware of the potential dangers on these two sections if busy with other walkers or cars. Even Colin, who was the only student who hadn't been on the Crib Goch ridge before, had heeded every word Simon had said to him on the approach and was treating it with the respect it deserved.

The scree path, if you can call it a path, which leads off Crib Goch and down to the road below, is one of the few places in Snowdonia that I would avoid whenever possible. But as part of the traditional fifteen Peaks route, it's essential. Getting the students to take their time on the scree was as difficult as Simon and I had expected. Peter and Colin in particular wanted to run down the scree, a choice I'd often made myself, but it wasn't a choice that Simon or I could allow the students to make. The road, when we reached it, brought welcome relief to all of us and the banter that had been subdued on the way down from the high ground returned, which seemed to make the remaining trek to Nant Peris happen in no time at all.

With everyone still in high spirits, we set off up Elidir Fawr from Nant Peris, our well-deserved, al fresco breakfast giving us renewed energy. With endurance, rather than difficulty, being the theme of the start of the second stage, we were able to chat more, and as we crossed a footbridge higher up the valley, the conversation was as easy as if we were enjoying a gentle walk in the country. But when six hundred metres higher, and still not having reached the first summit of the second stage, the conversation had all but stopped. It wasn't just the height gain, but the relentless boredom of putting one foot in front of the other for over an hour, with only the slope in front of you to look at, that drained our energy.

Once on Elidir Fawr's summit, though, the extensive views in all directions was the best remedy for any fatigue we were feeling. With a final admiring look at Marchlyn Mawr Reservoir, which supplies the Dinorwig Power Station in the mountain below where we were standing, we set off again on the downhill section towards Y Garn. The variation in terrain kept us going over Y Garn and, after a sustenance break at Llyn y Cwn, the steep ascent to the Glyders' ridge seemed less work than it should have been at this juncture.

On our practice run in the mist, we'd walked just below Castell y Gwynt and right past the Cantilever Stone, which we hadn't been able to see before. As we approached the Cantilever Stone – a long, finely balanced slab of rock, ideal for bouldering, which was used as the entrance to the dragon's lair in the 1981 film *Dragonslayer* – I found Priya and Eve's conversation amusing.

'Where did that come from?' Priya quizzed.

'It's the Cantilever Stone,' Simon informed the students.

'I'm sure that weren't here two weeks ago,' Eve said.

I chuckled to myself and then asked Colin, 'Do you think you could walk along it?'

Simon and I smiled as we'd already agreed on this location for a rest break, knowing it would allow time for Colin to climb onto the Cantilever Stone as compensation for not having been able to make the leap from Adam to Eve on our last mountain walk (which wasn't on our agenda for this one either).

'Smile then,' Enid shouted, as she took Colin's photograph as he sat cross-legged on the end of the stone.

Eve and Priya continued, for several minutes, to puzzle over how they could have been so close to the Cantilever Stone, but had no sight of it due to the dismal mist on their last visit.

With no mist to slow us down this time, we quickly arrived at the scree path that lies to the east of Bristly Ridge.

'More rubbish...' I could hear Peter muttering to himself as he kept slipping down a few centimetres with each step he took.

There was no time for another break at the saddle between the Glyders and Tryfan, and once on Tryfan's summit, we paused only briefly by Adam and Eve as we were conscious of the time. Just as the distance from the shoreline to the horizon of an ocean appears to be far shorter than it actually is, so it is with the view of Ogwen Cottage from the summit of Tryfan; it always takes longer to get there than you envisage it will. But, with the end of the second stage in view, we were all in good spirits as we started our descent down the Western Gulley of Tryfan.

We all looked forward to catching up with Little Dave at Ogwen Cottage and he'd brought Alice, along with Bethan and Tess, with him. Tess had joined the Ysgol Abaty roll at the start of the summer term. Almost as soon as she'd arrived, she and Bethan had become best friends. Tess wasn't at all like Bethan. She went about things in a calm and patient way, which had started to influence Bethan's thoughts and actions. This was a change in Bethan's personality, which all of the staff and several of the students were grateful for. This was the first time that Bethan had been allowed to go on a day out since her window-smashing foray when Colin had brushed aside her heartfelt affections.

We arrived at Ogwen Cottage far more tired than we'd been at Nant Peris. Also, much to my surprise, there to greet us were my wife and daughters. My wife Anne and I had passed on our love of the mountains and our desire for adventure to both Anneka, now in her early 30s, and our youngest daughter, Annabelle, who by the time she was fifteen, the same age as most of the students with me, had completed the Welsh 3000s three times and who took every opportunity she could to go walking or climbing in Snowdonia.

Seeing them sitting on the wall near the café, sipping their drinks, I shouted across to them happily:

'Hiya, *Ann*, fancy seeing you here!'

I received my usual response, when all three replied in unison, 'Hi there, *you!*'

'Which one's Ann?' Peter asked, with a confused expression on his face.

'All of them!' I proudly replied. 'My wife's name is Anne, and these are my daughters Anneka and Annabelle.'

Anne and I hadn't really thought about it at the time, but it does make life easier for me. I just have to say 'Ann' and at least one of them will answer. It doesn't always work, though. Sometimes they all ignore me, making out that they thought it was one of the other two I wanted.

This left Peter so confused that he forgot his chat-up lines and just sat on the wall pondering the three names, and whether I was winding him up or not.

This was probably a good thing. I've learned that both Anneka and Annabelle, with their athletic builds and long black hair, attract considerable attention from most of the males they come across – and even a few females. Their admirers, of course, are unaware of the fiery nature they possess, especially when they both want to get into the bathroom at the same time prior to a night out!

If Joe had been with us, I know he would have appreciated my usual punchline about the names of the women in my life:

'If I get forgetful in my old age, I'll only have to remember one name, and I'll be right every time,' I said and smiled.

Priya had spent the last two kilometres before we reached Ogwen Cottage walking at the back of the group with Enid. She'd complained of a stone, or something similar, in her shoe as we made our way up the steep rise from Llyn y Cwn. Enid had checked it out and found that a large blister had formed on the outside of the big toe on her right foot. Enid had protected it with a blister plaster and initially this had worked. However, the scree on the descent from the Glyders had taken its toll, bursting the blister. Her change of gait, to protect her right foot, had now produced a similar, though not burst, blister on the heel of her left foot. In keeping with her character, and not wanting to slow the pace of the group, Priya had said plainly to Enid:

'The next time we get to the minibus, I'm going to stop, cos it's not fair on the others.'

So, on reaching Ogwen Cottage, our party was, reluctantly, reduced to seven.

With a deep feeling of sympathy for Priya, we headed off without her on the final stage towards the summit of Pen yr Ole Wen. This was approximately twelve hours after we'd had our photograph taken on the summit of Snowdon, and it looked far higher and steeper than when we'd viewed it from the top of Tryfan.

Even when this ascent is the initial part of a walk, the steepness of the climb from Ogwen Cottage to the summit of Pen yr Ole Wen will take your breath away. After more than an hour of weary trudging, we reached the summit, where we found no sign of any other life. During the climb to the summit, I'm sure all of us had thought about Priya at least once, sitting in comfort at Ogwen Cottage, and wondered if staying there might have been a better option.

Once on the Carneddau ridge, all the long steep climbs were over. This was also the point of no return and we all knew that, except for injury, the seven of us would complete the Welsh 3000s. Even though sore feet were shared by many of us, the happy banter I now associate with my time at Ysgol Abaty had returned. But I knew that no one would suggest a run to Foel Fras, as Martin had the last time we were on the Carneddau.

We arrived at the final 3000 peak just as daylight was fading. Then again, we still had Drum to surmount.

Our recorded times were:

Snowdon to Carnedd Ugain – 16 minutes
Carnedd Ugain to Crib Goch – 37 minutes
Crib Goch to Nant Peris – 1 hour 43 minutes
Nant Peris rest – 51 minutes
Nant Peris to Elidir Fawr – 1 hour 39 minutes
Elidir Fawr to Y Garn – 1 hour 16 minutes
Y Garn to Llyn y Cwn – 34 minutes

Llyn y Cwn rest – 10 minutes
Llyn y Cwn to Glyder Fawr – 1 hour
Glyder Fawr to Glyder Fach – 42 minutes
Glyder Fach to Tryfan – 50 minutes
Cantilever Stone rest – 15 minutes
Tryfan to Ogwen Cottage – 54 minutes
Ogwen Cottage rest – 55 minutes
Ogwen Cottage to Pen yr Ole Wen – 1 hour 39 minutes
Pen yr Ole Wen to Carnedd Dafydd – 23 minutes
Carnedd Dafydd to Yr Elen – 1 hour 13 minutes
Yr Elen to Carnedd Llewelyn – 22 minutes
Carnedd Llewelyn to Foel Grach – 33 minutes
Foel Grach to Carnedd Uchaf – 15 minutes
Carnedd Uchaf to Foel Fras – 15 minutes

We made our way towards the minibus, using an old fence as a metaphorical handrail, a technique I've used many times when navigating at night or in misty conditions when features such as fences, walls or streams are available to follow. Having summited Drum en route as well, we finally arrived at Bwlch y Ddeufaen car park just as darkness engulfed us. Everyone was glad that the day's activity was over and that their boots could finally be taken off in the comfort of the minibus.

With the support of Simon and Enid, I'd managed to get the students to complete all of the peaks without any bursts of competitive running, and to have photographs taken on every peak as proof. This included Carnedd Uchaf, the mysterious 15th peak, which is often not singled out. Our total time was sixteen hours and twelve minutes, and on the journey home everyone, except Little Dave slept. Even Bethan, who never seemed to sleep, took the opportunity to have at least forty winks.

Chapter Fourteen
Memorable Events

July brought with it two memorable events, each one demanding its own unique preparations. The first one was a school inspection by ESTYN, the Welsh equivalent of England's OFSTED. This would involve a team from ESTYN visiting the school, so that they could 'provide advice and guidance' to the Welsh Government on quality and standards in education and training at Ysgol Abaty.

I've experienced four school inspections during my teaching life, and how times have changed! The first one was during my first year of teaching, at one of the most academically successful schools in England. Although fresh out of college, I was full of confidence and had a thorough knowledge of all my subjects. Showing the inspectors little in the way of paperwork, I simply taught my classes – while they observed and then happily chatted to the pupils afterwards.

One inspector asked me why I didn't teach one

specific technical process in a certain way. His suggestion was totally inappropriate and, in fact, dangerous, as it was a practical element of a Design and Technology lesson. I explained the failings of his proposed teaching method, and I asked him what his qualifications were in the subject. Telling me that he had none, I walked away, no doubt showing my feelings as I did so. The most constructive conversation we had wasn't actually about the lesson he'd just observed, but about skiing, as I had a display in the classroom of a school skiing trip to Austria which I'd taken part in. The inspector concerned was a keen skier himself, and it was about skiing in general that we chatted, rather than educational matters. The feedback I received throughout was excellent, and my colleagues and I seemed to pass through it without any difficulties or anxiety.

By the time my third school inspection had come around many years later, things had changed greatly. The emphasis was now on paperwork, and *more* paperwork. Teachers were preoccupied with the event long before it was scheduled to happen. Senior school staff would ask for files that showed detailed plans – long, mid and short-term. In fact, they wanted to see more paperwork than could possibly be read by them or anyone else – endless plans! And they didn't want to see if they were appropriate or beneficial to the students; they wanted to see if they'd please the ESTYN inspectors when they arrived.

To my great surprise, one excellent teacher went off work with stress before the inspection even started. I recall telling another young teacher, who was being drawn into this mass hysteria:

'I've never known a gifted teacher, in the eyes of the inspectors, to be given a pay rise, or a poor one to lose their job.'

In other words, inspections were, in general, a paper exercise (and there was a lot of paper involved!), and this seems to be the way of things in today's box-ticking educational system too.

Even among the staff of Ysgol Abaty – where every day there was a real possibility that you'd need to make a trip to the A&E Department of Glan Clwyd Hospital after you'd been assaulted by one of the students – the arrival of the ESTYN inspection team caused more concern than I would have thought possible.

We were all well prepared with our long, mid and short-term plans, all in new, colour-coordinated ring binders. Every teacher had their plans for the day placed in a prominent position on their desk, as well as a copy of the actual lesson plan to pass to any inspector who appeared in the classroom and who wished to observe the lesson. Of course, handing a copy of the lesson plan to an inspector was a risky business here; the very nature of the students attending Ysgol Abaty meant that hardly any lessons went to plan.

As usual, I was the first member of the teaching staff to arrive. I paused at the receptionist's hatch to chat to Susan. We'd become great friends, always seeing the funny side of what was happening around us. I, no doubt, had set the pattern for this on my first teaching day, when

Susan had walked into the visitor's toilet and found me in a state of undress, trying my best to clean up the muddy mess I'd created through no fault of my own.

Our usual morning conversations concerned any students who happened to be absent that day, along with any messages from parents or members of the public – perhaps a trivial complaint about something they thought was going to bring about the end of the world! Today, these were quickly bypassed so that we could discuss the inspection team.

Leaning through her hatch to gain my attention, Susan's said, 'The inspectors are here already and they've decided to make the History Room their base.' She raised her eyebrows as she spoke.

'What time did they arrive then?' I asked as I lent partway into the open hatch.

'Gareth had to come in at quarter to seven to open up for them,' Susan said in an unusually low voice.

'Wow, that's keen,' I whispered back.

'They're now enjoying a morning cuppa which I had to make for them – as if I haven't got enough to do. Apparently, they'll be in this early every morning to "plan their schedule" for the day.'

'Dai Twice won't be happy when he realises he's lost his History Room,' I concluded.

Then, smiling to myself, I made my way to the workshop so I could enjoy a morning cuppa and plan my own schedule for the day!

The staff briefing that followed was without the humour

and scepticism that usually interrupted the flow of proceedings. Mr Lewis, the Head of the Inspection Team, and one of his team members were attending. Although they were inspecting Ysgol Abaty, the close link between the school and the hostel meant that they'd require information on Pen-y-Bryn as well. A main part of the morning briefing usually included a handover from the hostel team to the school team, which was of particular interest to the inspectors as they didn't usually experience this.

Mr Lewis seemed to be a nice person, though his obviously expensive suit seemed out of place among the casual attire of the hostel and school staff.

'I'm here to see what you do *well* at Ysgol Abaty, rather than what you *don't*,' he stressed. Then he smiled. 'You know, I've never been to a school before where the teaching staff outnumber the students at times, and where it's impossible to tell which are the students and which are staff...' He chuckled to himself before continuing. 'It was far easier when the teachers wore mortar boards and cloaks, as they did in my schooldays!'

Fifteen minutes later, when I was in the office checking on an order of paint, Mr Lewis approached the receptionist's hatch. The humour had disappeared from his voice when he explained his situation.

'I have to let you know that someone has removed my wheel trims,' he said seriously to Susan.

Having gone to his car to collect some additional paperwork, he'd noticed that the trims were missing. Now this is where the sense of humour that I share with

Susan doesn't always go down very well. Mr Lewis had expected Susan to be shocked and horrified when he reported this incident to her. Instead, she simply replied:

'Welcome to Ysgol Abaty! Be grateful you still have your wheels.' Then she turned away to carry on with the photocopying she was doing.

Not the most diplomatic response, I'm sure, but it did set the scene for the inspectors of life at Ysgol Abaty and Pen-y-Bryn Hostel.

The inspection week was a busy one. Simon and Enid spent every day taking students out on trips; the fact that these students were that day's most volatile ones was just a coincidence, of course! To be fair, most of the students appreciated the situation and played their part over the week in gaining the school an excellent report. Some, like Michael and Priya, met the inspection team as representatives of the students. The inspectors were captivated by Michael's artwork and Priya's maturity.

Others, like Bethan, who perhaps were trying a little bit too hard to be good, showed the other side of the students' personalities. One example was when a carved wooden sculpture of a Welsh dragon went crashing through a window during a Welsh lesson being observed by Mr Hughes, who'd attended the first morning briefing with Mr Lewis. Mr Hughes had quickly, and wisely, left the room, fearing his presence might make the matter worse. Perhaps he also thought that the next flying dragon might be coming in his direction. Later that day, he made a point of catching up with Dai Twice, who'd been teaching at the time.

'Thank you for letting me observe an excellent lesson; I now realise why the staff-to-student ratio is so high.'

As the last of the inspectors drove off, Susan beckoned me over to her position behind the receptionist's hatch.

With a straight face, she asked, 'What's the difference between a plastic surgeon and a school inspector?'

I replied, 'I don't know.'

Grinning, she quipped, 'One tucks up features, and the other...' leaving me to inwardly finish the joke.

We both laughed out loud.

The second and far more enjoyable event in July – at least for me – was a return trip to Mount Snowdon. I always enjoyed my trips there and one of my favourite activities was racing the train. During the previous couple of weeks, my thoughts had kept returning to Eve's time of under thirty-four minutes; this was for the first eight kilometres of the Snowdon Marathon, a road section going from Llanberis to Pen y Pass. I'd now checked her time against the time of Tracy McCartney, who'd won the Snowdon Marathon in 2015. Tracy's time at Pen y Pass was thirty-two minutes and forty-seven seconds, causing me to cross-reference the result several times. Eve's time was slower, but only by a minute or so. Now I know Tracy went on to run another thirty-eight kilometres (in the equivalent flat distance) but, even so, I now knew what I'd suspected all along; Eve was indeed an exceptional and elite runner.

The race against the Snowdon train was to be a fun day out. The inspection was over and done with, and the general feeling around Ysgol Abaty and Pen-y-Bryn was a relaxed one. I was feeling full of confidence, as I'd survived almost a full school year at Ysgol Abaty. During my time here, I'd met a new member of staff at the morning briefing, only to discover that he'd given in his notice and walked off-site before the morning break! This had really puzzled me, as during my small talk with him, my impression of him was of just how well suited he was to the job. It seems that, depending on your character and personality, working at Ysgol Abaty can be the best place or the worst to be employed. For the time being at least, it was the best place for me.

Early on Saturday the 16th of July, I set off in my own car with Eve, Martin and Peter. We were going to run up and down the Llanberis Path, using the train as our pacemaker. As one train goes up the mountain, another comes down, and whether you're going up or down, the train journey lasts about an hour. As you might envisage, covering between seven and eight kilometres in about an hour, even taking into account the uneven and rocky path, sounds easy enough. In truth, the descent is easily managed, running literally downhill, or level, all the way. However, this is balanced out by the run up. As you start at about one hundred and twenty metres above sea level, the eight kilometres up to the summit have a height gain of about nine hundred and sixty metres, finishing at the highest point in the British Isles, excluding Scotland.

Psyched up and full of anticipation, the four of us set off as the 10:00am train left the station, its steam billowing in all directions as it pulled away, the smoke from the engine's firebox filling our lungs. Even before we reached the last of the houses on Victoria Terrace, Eve was disappearing out of sight around the left-hand bend, ahead of us. From then on, apart from Martin or Peter occasionally telling me that they could see her compulsory bright-yellow top in the distance, we didn't see her at all. Their young eyes were far better than my ageing ones at seeing distant objects, so whenever they informed me, 'There she is,' I smiled and always replied, 'Oh yes, I can see her!'

Having seen Eve disappear from view as we neared the Halfway Café, we'd decided the three of us would keep together on our way up, an idea I came to appreciate as we ran under the small railway bridge on the upper section of the path. The height gain, as we ran, had taken its toll on Peter, especially with so much of the gradient being in double figures.

Peter gasped, 'Can we jog slowly for a bit now?'

I happily replied, 'If that's OK with Martin, it's fine with me.'

Without a second's delay, Martin's response was, 'I'm fine running but we should stay together, shouldn't we?'

Peter's request had been like music to my ears and, judging by his rapid response, to Martin's as well. This resulted in the final section alongside the railway line being confined to a slow, relaxed pace. Exactly what I needed, as our pace on the lower half of the path, which had no doubt quickened due to seeing Eve stretching her lead ahead of us, was now having its effect on me. Peter's request to run more slowly meant that I was able to enjoy this last section, rather than just 'survive' it, as I usually did when I was on my own.

Martin, Peter and I had kept the train within sight for the first five kilometres. Then, as we hit a steeper section of the path, Bryn had left us behind. Not Bryn the maintenance man from Pen-y-Bryn Hostel, of course; this Bryn was the name of the steam engine that we'd used as our pacemaker, named after Sir Bryn Terfel, the Welsh opera star. Once we knew that the train had beaten us, we'd settled into a more comfortable pace for the most part, reaching the summit in less than one and a half hours.

My next, confirmed sighting of Eve was as we ran up the steps on the east side of the summit café. She was sitting next to the café wall, chatting to a couple of walkers and their yellow Labrador. The Labrador's tail was wagging madly in response to the fuss it was receiving, as the couple took photos of Eve and her new four-legged friend on Eve's phone. It was obvious that Eve had reached the summit a considerable amount of time before the three of us got there as she was completely relaxed – enjoying the morning sun and the enthusiastic attention of the Labrador.

After taking in the views, which allowed us to recover from the run, we joined Eve just as the Labrador and its owners were setting off on their return trek back down to Llanberis.

'Bye-bye, Carys,' Eve shouted as the dog trotted down the steps beside the café.

Sitting with Eve, while enjoying some well-earned

teas and pasties from the summit café, people-watching took over. The mix of people on the summit is always cosmopolitan when the trains are in operation. Most are walkers, but a few actually climb some of the sections on their ascent. Add to this the passengers who travel up on the train and the runners, like the four of us, and you'll discover that over three hundred and fifty thousand people now reach Snowdon's summit every year. There was a kaleidoscope of colours as we looked around, from the mountain wear of the outdoor enthusiasts to the casual clothes of the train passengers. Extreme weather clothing, running shorts, even mini dresses and high heels could be spotted. And all of these people were enjoying the best view in the UK, according to a recent poll.

Eve had also been beaten to the summit by the train. Even so, she'd matched its pace until the intersection between the Snowdon Ranger and Llanberis Paths. The multitude of walkers, and politeness on her part, had restricted her pace on this final section. With a look of disappointment on her face, she pulled back her sleeve and showed us her watch. The monochrome dial showed sixty-two minutes, twenty-three seconds. I only wished I could be so disappointed with such a time.

Then she explained, 'I followed your advice, Tom, and used the train as a pacemaker. It was a bit annoying, though, having to stop when it stopped at the station halfway up.'

'Really!' I replied.

I knew immediately that, in Eve, not only did I have an entry for a mountain marathon, I had an exceptional one. It had never occurred to me that Eve would stop as the train did on the way up. With hindsight, this is something I should have realised as her autism made her take things literally. I, on the other hand, had always used this intermission as a chance to gain an advantage over the train. This was easily justified, in my mind, because when I paused for a drink or to adjust a shoelace, the train never waited for me!

The run, or even jog, from the summit down to Llanberis is completely different to the run up. Rather than being preoccupied with pace, gradient and 'just keeping on going', you need to concentrate on safety – avoiding other mountain users and not losing your footing or taking a tumble. The four of us ran down together, waving to the train passengers as our routes came together and crossed each other. With a short sprint once we'd reached Victoria Terrace, we were able to be seated at the picnic tables near the station café before the train pulled in. This is an easy task for most runners, but remarkable for many of the passengers who'd been cheering us on from the train windows as we made our descent.

Sitting, enjoying our ice creams, I realised that, for the time being at least, I was sitting with friends and not just students. The day's outing had been a total success. Eve was the only one who seemed a little disappointed, due to her not getting to the summit at the same time as the train.

'There's a race called "The Eryri 32",' I said, to distract Eve from her disappointment. 'It's thirty-two kilometres long and includes the summit of Snowdon on its course.'

Eryri is the Welsh name for Snowdonia, and the race combines the best of the Snowdon Marathon and the Snowdon Race – though some competitors would argue that it combines the 'worst bits' of these two events. Eve's expression immediately changed, revealing her rare smile that could literally light up any room. She wanted to know everything about the race.

'When is it? Where does it start?' she asked and then, most importantly for her, 'When do I start training?'

Martin and Peter couldn't get a word in edgeways, so they carried on with their own conversation about the small group of girls who were queuing up at the ice cream kiosk. They'd been on the train that we'd used as our pacemaker on the way down, waving and shouting at Martin and Peter at every opportunity. Each one was proudly displaying a yellow cross on a blue background, which was sewn onto all of their rucksacks in various locations.

As they approached Martin and Peter, the four girls jostled for position as they loudly initiated the conversation. The girls chatted to the two lads happily, as if they were old friends, and good ones at that. Both Martin and Peter were taken aback by the friendliness of the girls. Then, just as they were starting to enjoy their celebrity status as 'train racers', the girls realised their bus was due to arrive. Quickly, they headed off towards the bus interchange on the other side of the main road, leaving the boys bitterly disappointed that their fame had faded so quickly.

'Do you think they live round here?' Peter asked me, no doubt considering a return trip to Llanberis if they did.

'I think you'll find they're Swedish,' I explained, as both boys looked puzzled.

'If they're from Sweden, how come they speak English?' Martin asked.

I then had to explain the ease with which most foreigners, especially those from Scandinavia, seem to speak English, as well as several other languages, and the disappointment I felt that we didn't have the same skill.

Martin stood up and asked, 'Can you borrow me a pen, so I can get their Facebook info?'

I had to suppress my teacher's urge to correct his use of English and to point out that the Swedish girls' English was actually better than his! At least in Wales there are many who can say they're fully bilingual, speaking Welsh and English as they please.

The Swedish girls' departure, waving from the back window of the bus, seemed to be the cue for our own departure. We made our way back to my Fabia, the bright white paintwork making it easy to find among the other, mainly silver, cars in the car park.

Arriving back at Pen-y-Bryn, Martin and Peter were full of the fact that they'd run against and beaten the train. They excluded the fact that this was only on the way down. Eve was quiet, though – still disappointed that she hadn't beaten it going up as well.

Although Joe hadn't been with us during the

Snowdon adventure, it was his contribution to the day's events that had me smiling all the way from Pen-y-Bryn to Pant, as I drove home. Eve had been showing everyone the pictures she'd taken during the day to record the event. She passed the phone around the group, so everyone could see. She was especially enthusiastic about the photos of her and the affectionate Carys, the yellow Labrador at the summit café.

Joe, when he saw the photos of Carys, disclosed, 'We had two Labradors at home when I was little. First one was called Tess, then we got another one and I wanted to call it Tickle. I told me mum it was cos she loved being tickled behind the ears. Mum thought it was OK, even when I told her that when I wanted them both to come, I could shout, "Tess and Tickle, come here!" or even better, "Tess! Tickle!" which is quicker...'

Joe looked around to make sure everyone was following his storyline, then, finding it impossible not to laugh as he gave his punchline, he added, 'Me mum still said it was OK, with me calling me new puppy Tickle, until I said I could just shout "Balls!" really loud if I wanted the dogs to come superfast... Then me mum said I had to call me new puppy Sandy.'

Chapter Fifteen
A New Academic Year

School summer holidays are often thought of as being one of the perks of being a teacher. In fact, they're usually filled with teachers trying to leave the memories of the previous year behind them and making preparations for the year ahead. The special nature of Ysgol Abaty and its four-term year meant that just the four weeks of August made up the entire summer holiday.

Eve's only topic of conversation during the last week of July had been the Eryri 32. There had been a couple of weeks at the end of May when Eve had considered leaving Ysgol Abaty at the end of the current school year, but after a lot of consideration, she'd decided to put off leaving until Christmas.

'I want to get an A or A* in my Maths, as it's my best subject,' she'd said to Dai Twice, even though she had already achieved a very impressive B in her Mathematics GCSE.

Dai Twice was more than happy to have a possible A

or even A* in Mathematics by an Ysgol Abaty student, so he quickly agreed, saying, '*Da iawn*, Eve, with your skill and my ability, an A or A* in Maths it is then.'

I think Eve was actually staying until Christmas so she could train and take part in the Eryri 32 race, and as I was solely responsible for putting the idea into her head, I felt duty-bound to support her to the utmost in this task.

Knowing that Eve, as usual, was spending the summer holiday period at Pen-y-Bryn, I left her a two week training schedule for the start of August, when I would have my own family holiday. Leaving Eve to complete the schedule without supervision didn't concern me at all. I knew, as always, that she'd follow the programme to the letter.

My number one concern, however, was that all the places for this year's Eryri 32 had already been taken. Eve would have to go on a reserve list and hope that a place would become available. Eve's reaction to this was mixed; she was disappointed that she wasn't assured a place, but she was still eager to train as if she had one. This was because, as she had already assured me, she was adamant she would get a place.

As always, for me, the final week of the summer holidays had gone by too quickly. As I parked up below the tall poplar trees, once again I took a moment and recalled my first day at Ysgol Abaty. A mixture of enthusiasm and apprehension had seen me through the events of that day and, although still in a state of utter astonishment as I drove home, I'd hesitantly come back the next day and now, here I was, still returning a year later.

Now, surprisingly, instead of thinking about the students who I would have preferred to have 'moved on' from Ysgol Abaty over the summer break, I was thinking about the ones I would have preferred to stay. Stephen and his 'shadow' Yorkie had both gone back to their home areas. During the time they'd spent together at Ysgol Abaty, though very different in character, they'd become great friends. This was demonstrated by Stephen in February when George, one of the students from Ysgol Weirglodd, wouldn't enter a race in the cross-country competition. This can often happen as some students find it difficult to accept failure and opt instead not to take part. Two non-teaching staff had tried to encourage George to participate in the race. This had been witnessed by Yorkie.

'What do you think's wrong over there then?' he'd asked the lads around him.

Most of the group had carried on with their own jesting about the situation. Joe, though, had replied with the witticism, 'He's lost his bottle hasn't he.'

This prompted Yorkie to approach the staff and offer to help them find George's 'lost bottle'.

Returning to the group, Yorkie broke the news to Joe. 'He hasn't lost his bottle; he just prefers not to enter the race today.'

Before Joe and the rest could chastise Yorkie, Stephen had controlled the situation by saying, 'Don't worry, mate, we all know you always want to help others; that's why we all like you.'

Realising the truth in Stephen's statement, the lads had let Yorkie's perfect example of an idiom not being understood by someone on the autistic spectrum go unchallenged. I hoped the distance between them now wouldn't bring an end to their friendship. Stephen, in particular, was a student of whom I'd grown fond of at Ysgol Abaty, particularly as he was there through no fault of his own. I'd like to think he'll return to North Wales in a few years' time and tell us how well he's doing.

Priya had also left. After completing the application forms, and a series of interviews and fitness tests, the King's Royal Hussars had accepted her. If you're going to join up, then what better name for your regiment to have than that? It immediately suggests loyalty, history and triumphant victory. Priya's mum had happily signed the parental consent forms and, with glowing references from both Gareth Lee and Little Dave, as head teacher and head of hostel respectively, Priya had completed the rest of the process herself.

The running club training sessions that she'd attended meant that she completed the required 2.5 kilometre run with ease in less than twelve minutes. Although Joe's main love interest was Eve, he was at heart a natural ladies' man. Realising just how much Priya had wanted to join the army, he'd spent the summer term running his own personal 'boot camp' for Priya. Working in particular on exercises that would improve her strength, like sit-ups and press-ups, he'd also succeeded in enabling her to breeze through the 'Beep' test. This was Joe's support at its best.

Of course, as well as a number of students moving on, September, in common with other schools, brought new arrivals. I always think that each new school year can be compared to the Atlantic tides. Unfortunately, the waves coming in are always more problematic than the ones going out. After three weeks of near-perfect lessons with Alan, Roy, Martin and Joe (the remaining students from *Shakespeare* from my first year), the atmosphere was completely shattered by the arrival of Johnny.

How can Johnny best be described? Well, you need to think of Taz, or to use his official name, Claude, an animated Warner Brothers' cartoon character. Based on a Tasmanian devil, Taz achieved huge popularity in the 1990s. Anyone with knowledge of both Johnny and Taz would acknowledge the many characteristics they share.

Johnny's introduction to me was a dramatic one. Waiting for *Shakespeare* to arrive, the silence outside the workshop was suddenly shattered by a commotion. Now, this gives every member of staff working at a special school or hostel two choices: you either occupy yourself in your own comfort zone, so that you can legitimately excuse your absence from the cause of the commotion, or, which unfortunately is always my reflex and preferred option, you can immediately head towards the source of the noise and get fully involved, if necessary. I've always felt that it's an unwritten rule to fully support other members of staff. I also feel more secure and safe in the knowledge that this, hopefully, brings about a reciprocal action when required!

So, as often happens at Ysgol Abaty, I was in a

situation that I hadn't expected to be in a few seconds earlier. Standing in the corridor outside the classroom with Alan, Roy and Martin, I was for once looking down at Little Dave who was sitting on the floor and holding Johnny in his arms, in a similar way to a mother cuddling a baby. Even with Little Dave's huge size and strength, Johnny was managing to release his own arms and legs, almost in a timed rotation, from Little Dave's grasp. Without being instructed to, Joe had gone for help, leaving the others wondering whether they should support Little Dave or stand back and enjoy the spectacle.

My arrival on the scene prompted the boys to ask, 'Do you want us to help, Tom?'

Unfortunately, the answer from any member of staff has to be 'no' every time, even though, practically, they could have lent a hand. The exception, of course, is when they go to alert other members of staff about the situation, which Joe had already gone to do. So, it was up to me alone to help Little Dave get hold of the flailing limbs.

To an inexperienced observer, grabbing an arm or both arms might appear to be the best course of action to take. After all, the legs are stronger than the arms and usually have footwear attached, which is an additional concern. However, my preference is for the lower rather than the upper limbs, having experienced and witnessed headbutts, bites and the worst thing, psychologically rather than physically, spitting. I always tend to go for holding one leg or, if possible, both legs. The other advantage of this is that the culprit tends to remember, with displeasure, those 'in his face' rather than those near his feet.

Needless to say, my lesson plan for *Shakespeare* didn't materialise. Once Joe had returned with Gareth, the four boys joined Alice's class, no doubt for impromptu drinks and cakes. As a result of Johnny maintaining his disruptive actions for the rest of the morning, Little Dave, Gareth and I missed our own elevenses. Later, we concluded that the reason for Johnny's frantic behaviour was that he was nervous of a new experience: being taught by me for the first time!

I'm pleased to say that when I met Johnny in the hostel later that same evening, he demonstrated none of his morning's misbehaviour. I joined a group of the older lads for tea, which was a large quantity of chilli con carne and rice with a scoop of natural yogurt. Joe, just as he'd done with Priya and her fitness training, seemed to have taken a positive and responsible approach towards Johnny. After finishing our meals, Joe, Johnny, Bethan and I took over the pool table, while just about everyone else watched one of the most popular DVDs from the hostel's film library: *Road House* starring Patrick Swayze.

So, as I was racking the pool balls for our fourth game – me and Johnny against Joe and Bethan – I pondered the scene around me. Johnny wasn't only a reasonable pool player, he was being a gentleman to all around him. But what I hadn't realised was that Bethan was, without doubt, a pool whizz! From the moment she had a cue in her hand, a different personality overcame her. She stood still and was patient, when not playing herself, and when it was her turn, she studied the layout of the balls carefully before taking her shot. She had a range of shots, including a delicate, almost slow-motion one, and accurate screw backs, through to some of the most powerful cannon shots I've ever seen played. Three games down and I realised that our losing streak was undoubtedly going to continue. In the previous game, Joe had taken the break, Johnny had potted one ball but missed his second pot, and I hadn't had the chance to pot any as Bethan had cleared the table.

Even though Bethan was maintaining her professional standards, she couldn't prevent her expression from portraying some amusement at my disbelief in her ability. Usually poker, even stern-faced, her smile was now even producing dimples which I hadn't realised she possessed.

She later explained to me that even though there was no evidence of it during the daytime, she hardly slept at night as her mind was always so active. Prior to coming to Pen-y-Bryn, The Grange Care Home, which she'd attended from the age of seven to eleven, had two resources that she'd taken full advantage of: a full-sized snooker table and a member of the hostel staff who was working nights there called James. James, apparently, not only had a personality that Bethan responded to, but he was also a gifted semi-professional snooker player.

Rather than have Bethan spend the night getting into mischief, James had introduced her to the game of snooker. They'd spent many nights playing into the early hours of the morning, while listening to some soothing music. This not only had a calming effect on Bethan and kept her out of trouble, but within a year of arriving at

The Grange, Bethan was able to make an occasional 50+ break during some of her nightly sessions at the table. By the time she'd had to move on to Pen-y-Bryn, having reached secondary-school age, she was able to give James a good game, even beating him on some occasions. The term 'fruits of a misspent youth' couldn't have been more appropriate. However, I had to put Bethan's 'cue' expertise to one side for now, I had more than enough to do keeping track of Eve's preparation for the Eryri 32.

As expected, when I met Eve for breakfast on the first Sunday after my holiday, she'd trained to perfection, as she'd promised she would. She'd warmed up for ten minutes beforehand and cooled down for five minutes after every training session, just as if I'd been there with her; this had comprised easy running and stretching, but was essential to avoid injury. Luckily, an injury was something Eve had never yet experienced.

After breakfast, we set off on our run. This was at a good pace, but within my comfort levels. The rolling hills of the Clwydian Range, a designated area of outstanding natural beauty, created the perfect training ground for us. A mixture of forests, heather-dressed summits, hill forts and, not forgetting, fantastic views, it was always a joy to be on the hills unless the weather was exceptionally harsh. Forty minutes later, we were back at the car and enjoying the spectacular view from Bwlch Pen Barras, over Ruthin to the hills beyond.

Pen y Ball Hill was perfect for the second training session of the week. This time my role would be as a coach, not a runner. I'd decided to train with Eve for the two easier training sessions that I'd planned. I would then leave Eve to take on the two more difficult sessions at a pace she decided – one which I knew I couldn't match. This second session involved running two, three and four minute repetitions: steady, fast and then racing speed, consecutively. A minute of recovery time, then go again. Eve's downhill recovery walk allowed me to stay in contact with her all the time. Eve completed five of these repetitions in about an hour. Bear in mind that most people get out of breath just walking up Pen y Ball Hill!

The third session suited my ability perfectly, so Eve and I set off together on a fifty minute run. I let Eve set the pace, as she seemed to have an inbuilt stopwatch, only looking at her actual one to confirm her own natural timing. We ran fast for five minutes and then jogged for a minute. After the seventh jog, we finished with eight minutes of fast running. Keeping up with Eve was harder than I'd expected, made worse for me, psychologically, by her relaxed running style.

Eve's last session of the week was a twenty-one kilometre run, once again on the Clwydian Hills. I let Eve choose her route and pace. I knew that I'd only slow her down, so I chose to have a rest day.

By the last Sunday in September each of the training sessions had increased, with Eve's solo run on the last session being twenty-six kilometres. With gradual increases, after another three weeks, we'd accomplished the hardest week's training. The comfortable run was only five minutes longer than the first run we'd undertaken after my holiday. However, it covered a far greater distance because both of our fitness levels had increased. In a similar way, the second and third sessions were harder in content, with much improved results achieved. The week's final training session for Eve was a run from Bodfari to Gyrn, a miniature summit about one and a half kilometres south of Foel Fenlli, and back. She mainly used the Offa's Dyke Path, which opened as a national trail in 1971. This resulted in a full distance of over thirty-six kilometres.

With only four weeks to go before the event, I think I was more nervous than Eve – in fact, I knew I was! Rather than concentrate on the distance involved, I'd decided that the height gain and terrain were more important. Also, I'd added a further element to Eve's training. Unless concentrating on sprint work, I'd give Eve a rucksack to run with. This was a technique that I'd used myself when training for mountain marathons. So I hunted out one of my many old Kimm sacks, which is a light rucksack, and lined it with a rolled-up foam camping mat for comfort. I then placed four steel boules balls down the centre of the mat. When this is done correctly, to avoid excess movement, you have a perfect aid to prepare for the physical exertion of mountain-marathon running.

I'd decided at the start that I'd keep Eve's weekly training schedule to the same format throughout the build-up to the race. With the distances and pace now reduced, I could join Eve on some of the 'easy' runs. Eve seemed to enjoy my company when we ran together, and

265

Bodfari

Penycloddiau

Moel Arthur

Moel Dywyll

Moel Famau

Offa's Dyke
Path

Jubilee Tower
on Moel Famau

Moel
Fenlli

Gyrn

*Route 11: Training run from Bodfari to Gyrn
and return: Approximately 36 kilometres long
and 1,270 metres' height gain.*

she was amused at my efforts to maintain the same pace as her.

'Are you OK, Tom?' seemed to be asked far too often for my liking.

I was able to get my own back on the hill intervals, as she tackled the various steep slopes of the Clwydians. As Eve carried out the different sets and distances, I was able to relax as I observed, encouraged and recorded her performances. However, much to my exasperation, there never seemed to be an appropriate juncture to ask, 'Are you OK, Eve?'

To my great relief, three weeks before race day, Eve got a letter confirming that she had a place on the Eryri 32. Eve's confidence in securing a place had been well founded; however, it did mean that, somewhere, another hopeful competitor would probably be bitterly disappointed.

To avoid boredom setting in for Eve, I conscripted Martin and Joe into the training camp for the last four sessions before the marathon. The only thing I couldn't understand was why I hadn't chosen this option, of being warm and dry inside Holywell Leisure Centre earlier, as the activity I offered on a Sunday was now during the colder and wetter months. Having taken a shine to Joe, Bethan was determined to get 'beach body' fit, so she'd volunteered to join the sessions herself and brought Tess along with her.

'Awesome, for sure,' was Tess' reaction to joining the sessions.

I have to admit that after the first lesson of mine that Tess had attended, I'd asked Helen whether Tess had lived in America.

'No, she's actually from Caernarfon!' she'd said, with a smile on her face.

Her parents had even apologised to Dai Twice about her accent when he was showing them around the school. It seems that Tess just likes the accent and uses it naturally now.

I liked the idea of Eve being a role model for Bethan, and with Tess present as well, I felt sure Bethan would continue with her positive progress. So, all in all, I was quite happy to spend part of my Sunday hostel shift training with them in the leisure centre. Alternating between resistance and cardio machines was the perfect way for Eve to train and keep motivated. I also saw it as a future means of social interaction for the five students. Many of the great friends I've made over the years I've met through sports-related activities.

Martin and Joe were having their end-of-session competition to see who could bench press the heaviest weight when I made the mistake of jinxing things by thinking: *What a perfect afternoon.*

Then I heard it.

Bethan's scream was deafening inside the Resistance Room. I turned in her direction. She was standing against the wall, pale with fright.

Tess was lying on the cushioned aerobic area of the floor, thankfully nowhere near any of the weight stations. I hadn't witnessed a scene like this before but having read

Tess' file, I immediately knew she was having a seizure. Of course, I'd considered what I might do if anything like this were to happen, but all the same I was anxious about the situation.

I approached Tess, instinctively telling Joe, 'Get a member of staff now!'

Joe was out of the room in seconds.

'It's OK,' I assured the other students as I knelt down beside Tess.

Although Tess' face, neck and arms were jerking repeatedly, I reasoned she could cause herself little injury by this. Her face was still a healthy colour and her lips weren't turning blue. So, though still very concerned, I said as many reassuring comments as I could think of to her.

Just as Joe returned with a young lifeguard, Tess stopped shaking. I sighed, believing I could start to relax now. But I wasn't prepared for the next stage of the episode; a sudden stiffness transformed Tess' upper body and it stunned me.

Thankfully, the lifeguard said reassuringly, 'Don't worry, it's only been a minute or two and she's coming out of it now.'

Then, much to my surprise, the stiffness in Tess' limbs subsided as quickly as it had occurred. Within a minute, she sat up by herself. She recognised her surroundings straight away.

'Gee, I know – I've had another one,' she said, seeming totally unperturbed.

Eve was now standing next to a tearful Bethan, who'd

been particularly upset by what had happened.

Trying to calm and soothe everyone, I said, 'It's over now. Everything's fine.' Though I knew I was saying this for my own benefit as well.

I knew Tess' notes stated: 'No need for ambulance or hospital admission if seizure is short and Tess is fully recovered within five minutes.' But, all the same, I was glad that the leisure centre had automatically called an ambulance. The paramedics who arrived a few minutes later agreed with the assessment in Tess' notes and after a quick examination, we were all allowed to return to the hostel.

Before setting off for Pen-y-Bryn, I phoned Dianne in *Berwyn* to warn her about what had happened. I couldn't help worrying about Tess as I drove the short distance back to Pen-y-Bryn. The boys chatted quietly to each other during the journey while Eve and I talked to Tess. Bethan, though, took me by surprise as she kept trying to hold Tess' hand, much to Tess' frustration.

Dianne greeted us as we arrived at the hostel and I thanked all the students for being so calm and helpful – especially Joe. Once we were inside, I had a quiet word with Bethan too.

'Thank you for letting me know so quickly that Tess wasn't well. It really helped her and me.'

I remember that, though still shaky, one of Bethan's rare smiles appeared on her face when she realised she'd helped in some way.

Then I made my way to the office to do two things. The first was to phone the leisure centre to thank them.

In particular, I praised the young lifeguard whose calm supervision had been so professional. And the second thing – well, that was to start filling out all the required paperwork!

Chapter Sixteen
Competitive Spirit

Tuesday, 1st November, All Saints' Day, had arrived. Where does the time go? It felt like I'd only just spent the evening drawing out a three-month training programme for Eve. Yet, here I was, all too quickly, having dinner with Eve and Bethan four days before Eve was to take part in the Eryri 32. All the training sessions were completed, all the running gear selected. All Eve had to do was relax for the next few days, undertake some short runs and then take part.

Eve found that relaxing on the day before the race was more difficult than it normally would be as the 'reserve' date for the North Wales Special Schools' Athletics Competition was now on that Friday. Several days of heavy rain in June had caused the original date to be postponed. So here we were, at the start of November, having a summer athletics meeting. Within the world of special education, this didn't raise any comments; the date was the last thing that would concern members of staff. Eve, of course, would have had great success at the meeting and she now found it difficult to understand why she couldn't enter the competition as well as maintain her own training regime.

Colin had waited for this day ever since the June competition had been postponed. Full of pent-up energy, and without any fear, he'd developed an interest in pole-vaulting. Not that he'd ever actually completed a pole vault. His initial interest had been ignited after seeing a programme on the Canadian pole-vaulter Robin Bone[15]. Because of Colin's enthusiastic sharing of his knowledge of pole-vaulting, and of Robin Bone, I now have a comprehensive knowledge of both. I do wonder, though, if it's Robin's vaulting ability or the aesthetically pleasing image she projects that first got Colin's attention.

Not having the opportunity to follow in Robin Bone's footsteps as a pole-vaulter (it's not an event that any special school would want included on its programme!), Colin had decided to become a triple jumper instead. He'd marked out a jumping board on the flat area near Pen-y-Bryn Hostel, and usually attempted at least one triple jump there every day as he passed by, much to the amusement of the other students. Bethan was the only one who seemed to fully support his efforts; perhaps she was trying to achieve some sporting success herself, though in Bethan's case, it was all about the image and not the winning that mattered.

Whenever he had the chance, Colin also took himself off to the high school that some of the Ysgol Abaty students attended on a part-time basis and practised there, using their jumping board and sand pit.

As none of the special schools have adequate athletics facilities, there has always been a tradition of using the facilities at one of the local high schools in North Wales for any sporting events. At Ysgol Abaty, we were delighted to know that one of the high schools near us had volunteered its excellent facilities for this occasion. This involved reduced travelling time for our students and meant it would be in a familiar environment, hopefully meaning that fewer incidents would take place.

On the day of the meeting, the students were spread out all over the field, so it was impossible for one member of staff to support them all. Each student could enter a maximum of three events.

Colin had decided to concentrate all his efforts on the triple jump. Despite the KS3 Boys' Triple Jump competition not taking place until 11:30am, he seemed to appear at my side every five minutes, saying:

'You'll watch me jump, won't you, Tom?'

'Of course I will, Colin. You just let me know when it's your turn,' was now more of a reflex reply than an answer to his question.

So I had little choice but to head towards the jumping area for his event when it finally occurred. Eve was helping me to keep a record of the students' results and looked even more like a member of staff as she held her clipboard and jotted things down carefully. In truth, I was occupying her mind, to ease her frustration at not being a competitor herself. Halfway across the field to the jumping pits, Colin seemed to appear out of nowhere and joined us, still bursting with enthusiasm for his event. We watched the final two long jumpers take their run-ups and applauded loudly at their jumps. Colin showed off his knowledge of the event:

'They'd jump better if they'd paced out a marker to know where to start their run-up instead of just guessing,' he said.

I was suitably impressed by Colin's knowledge and realised how seriously he was taking his event when he started pacing out the start of the run-up for his own jumps, before the other triple jumpers arrived.

Now, every so often, even when everything is done with the best intentions, it all goes disastrously wrong. With the long jumps complete, Rhys Jones, as always looking the part in his official Ysgol Weirglodd tracksuit, beckoned to the group of triple-jump competitors to follow him. Twenty metres further on, towards the corner of the field, the triple-jump area had just been cleared of weeds and prepared. With each step Colin took, he became quieter and more reticent. You could literally hear, and see, the enthusiasm draining from him as he followed the others to the corner of the field.

Wanting to keep his talent hidden, no one had actually seen Colin perform his jumps at the high school. He'd improved his distances, with continued practice, and was landing a reasonable length into the sand pit, which is a great achievement for any novice jumper. Unfortunately, his height of four foot six inches and corresponding ability, as well as the overgrown state of the jumping areas, had led him to confuse the locations of the long jump and the triple jump. We were quickly to discover that, when using the triple-jump area, Colin couldn't reach the sand!

But this is where luck, thankfully, played its part. It turned out that, due to there being a maximum of only three events per competitor and the lack of popularity of the triple jump, Colin was the only KS3 boy competing. So, it all turned out well, with Colin winning his age group category. Though I'm sure his admiration for Robin Bone would continue, I wondered if he'd enter the triple jump ever again.

The Ysgol Abaty runners had many successes during the athletics competition, but that already seemed like a distant memory. Now all our thoughts were on today, as the morning of Eve's race had arrived. I didn't even register that the 5th of November was also Guy Fawkes Night.

I found that, as I was travelling to Pen-y-Bryn, I was mentally rehearsing the events of the day. After the third loop of this process, I decided to try and relax by listening to the latest Ward Thomas[16] album, *Cartwheels*. This is a compromise between my love of traditional country music and the current popular music scene. I wanted to have some 'street cred' when giving students a lift, if they looked through my selection of CDs. Hopefully, by the end of the day, there'd be reason for everyone to be performing 'cartwheels', in light of Eve's success!

Entering the hostel dining room, I found Eve and her support team sitting near the serving hatch finishing off their drinks. Always popular with the other students, many had initially considered going to Snowdonia with Eve to encourage her. However, once the day's schedule was discovered, their enthusiasm had waned. So, sitting around the table were Martin, Joe, Alice, Bethan, Tess, Enid and Simon.

Simon had worked on the previous night shift, so wasn't able to go to Snowdonia with us for the day. He had, though, found time to complete the minibus checks and fill it with fuel. He'd completed many mountain races himself, including the Eryri 32 in 1999, when it was known as the Eryri 20 as miles were used rather than kilometres at that time. He'd managed to finish within the top four hundred runners – a great achievement when you consider there were about two thousand five hundred competitors that year. His shift had finished at 8:00am, but he wanted to wave Eve off as she left, which was typical of him.

At 8:20am precisely, we were all in the minibus and, with an enthusiastic shout of 'Good luck!' from Simon, we set off for Llanberis.

The start time of the race was 10:00am, so we had an hour and forty minutes to complete the journey, park up and go through Eve's final preparations, including a strict set of warm-ups that I'd developed for her.

The weather was nigh on perfect as we drove past Moel Siabod on our left. It was near the lower slopes opposite Moel Siabod, on the right of the A5, where I'd first realised that Eve might have a great natural running ability – though I hadn't realised back in November just how much of an effect Eve's initial race would have on my next twelve months.

Arriving at Llanberis, the volunteer marshals were out in force with welcoming smiles and using appropriate hand signals. We followed the car in front to an adjacent parking spot. Without doubt, the car's two occupants were amused when they saw how the students, almost literally, fell out of our minibus. With plenty of time to register, I walked Eve slowly over to the final registration tent. This left the others to take in the busy scene around them. Vehicles were coming onto the parking field at a rate of about one every fifteen seconds. Some only had competitors in them, but others, like our minibus, had spectators who were outnumbering the entrants. As Eve and I queued up to register, I looked back towards the minibus. At an estimate, I'd say that four thousand people were about to take part in or support the race. But noticing other supporters lining the course, the actual number of people experiencing the event would probably be double this number.

Even though we'd followed our pre-race timeline perfectly, the time for Eve to leave us and join the runners had come more quickly than we'd expected. With her banana consumed and our final best wishes given, Eve set off into the ever-increasing crowd of competitors.

Martin assured us by saying, 'Don't worry, I know how to find you again,' as he set off behind Eve to see her off at the start of the race.

'Martin, look for the minibus!' shouted Enid as the two of them headed off in the direction of the starting line.

Within a minute, they were both completely hidden from us. But just as Eve had a race plan to follow, we had a spectator one.

'Do you think Eve will be alright?' Enid asked as she spotted Martin heading back towards the minibus.

'She'll be fine, don't worry. Here's Martin now,' I cheerfully replied, trying to hide my own nerves. 'Everything OK, Martin?'

'Eve's sound, Tom; she pushed her way through everyone to be right at the front.'

She'd taken my advice from the Clogwyn Manod Circuit back in November as gospel: 'Only let two runners get ahead of you.' When the starting siren shrieked, Martin could see her in the third row from the front, with just two men between her and the starting tape – an ideal starting position. It was no surprise to me that Eve had remembered my advice. There is a saying, 'Elephants never forget'. I don't have much personal experience of elephants, but I can assure you, knowing Eve's location on the spectrum, there's little of any value that she ever forgets. If only the last piece of advice was as easy to achieve: 'Two hundred metres from the end, get into second place, and one hundred metres from the finish line, overtake the person in front of you and stay in front.'

The first thing we had to do, as spectators, was relax. It's always tremendously difficult to make your way to a preferred viewing position, because everyone else seems to want to find the same vantage point. The Eryri 32 route, because of its difficulty of access, made this particularly true. I decided that the best plan was to enjoy a leisurely cup of tea and a bacon sandwich or beef burger from one of the catering vans, and to take in the stunning views of the mountains around us with their peaks shrouded in morning mist. This was enthusiastically endorsed by the others.

My daydreams were interrupted by Enid and Joe's fits of laughter. Their amusement quickly spread around the rest of our group, who were also giggling.

Apparently, with tomato sauce seeping from the corners of her mouth, Tess had commented, 'Gee, this hamburger with ketchup sure is awesome.'

This had led to some joshing between the students about Tess' acquired accent, and Enid had explained to them:

'The regional accent from Gwynedd, where Tess used to live, is called 'Cofi' and it's very distinct in Wales.' She then demonstrated it with a phrase or two, 'Weather's nice, *aye*. Lots of people here, *aye*. Eve's in the race, *aye*.'

This fascinated the students, but it was the task that Enid had set Tess that had caused the hysterics. She'd asked Tess to spell Mississippi, a popular North Walian joke. Every time Tess tried, it came out as:

'M aye double S aye double S aye double P aye.'

Try as she might, Tess couldn't avoid sounding Caernarfon 'born and bred', with no evidence of an American accent anywhere. The more it frustrated Tess, the louder the laughter became. Personally, I was just pleased that Tess was feeling like her old self again.

With our slightly early 'elevenses' out of the way – and delicious it was too – there was still plenty of time to wander around the various pop-up stalls and chat to other spectators who were also trying to make the best use of this vacant period between the start and finish of the race. As the race had started at 10:00am, if all went well, I expected to see Eve crossing the finishing line at about 12:15pm at the earliest. Looking at my phone, I noted that it was now 10:28am. So I decided there was enough time to stretch our legs by wandering over to Llyn Peris to have a quick look at the Dinorwig Power Station, a popular tourist attraction, and I reminded Martin that he'd walked over it when summiting Elidir Fawr.

As we walked down the track towards the power station, Martin took great pleasure in pointing out the path up Elidir Fawr on the far side of the lake. He quickly named the Welsh 3000s, from Snowdon through to Foel Fras, and amazed Bethan by saying that he'd completed the route in sixteen hours. It seemed that Martin, in line with many other walkers and runners, achieved a far faster time as the event receded further into history. He was already twelve minutes faster than when he'd actually completed the challenge.

A slow stroll back and we were in perfect time to choose an excellent viewing spot about fifteen metres before the finish line, with its huge sponsored banner hanging above it. The official race clock was showing an elapsed time of 01.44.12 and we could already hear the echoes of spectators' cheers from the slopes above us.

'I do hope Eve's alright. It's such a long race,' Enid said.

'She'll be fine. I didn't hear any Scottish accents or medical talk from any of the other runners...' I joked.

Enid looked baffled.

'I'll explain later,' I said. 'Now you just need to relax.'

Enid's look of bewilderment reminded me that not everyone has my knowledge of the current elite runners. Finlay Wild[17], for example, a GP in Lochaber, holds many fell-running records and has won the Ben Nevis Race every year since 2010.

Competing with Eve were approximately two thousand five hundred other runners. Most of them were from Europe, though in among them were runners from as far away as New Zealand. Traditionally, Italians would lead the ascent up to Pen-y-Pass. Not surprising really, as most of the Italian mountain races only involve going up!

In the same way that Italian men are known for their ascent running, the home countries – Scotland, England, Ireland and Wales – usually produce the winning females. So, Eve found herself being followed closely by three female runners: French, Scottish and Irish respectively. More importantly, though, she was within sight of the lead runners, and running effortlessly.

Eve would also have to be careful not to collide with the many non-racers on the route. Some were there as spectators, others were walkers, surprised to find themselves on a race track!

As expected, following Eve's first run from Llanberis

to Pen y Pass, she'd completed the first stage comfortably. The first half of the race was in reality a road race. Once at the Pen-y-Gwryd Hotel, you had to turn right until you reached the edge of the Llyn Gwynant campsite. Here, you hair-pinned back on yourself and followed the Old Roman Road to reach Pen-y-Gwryd again. A path on the lower side of the road then takes you up to Pen-y-Pass for a second time, where you take on the Pyg Track. By the time the runners reach this point, they're spread out, looking like a length of bunting flags from a distance. Which is just as well as the steep, uneven path suggests a stumble at nearly every stride.

As the lead runners pass through the gate just after the junction for the Crib Goch Path, mist can drift in and out of nowhere – not that any of the runners pay attention to the beautiful scenery around them. Here the path is at its most difficult. You have to attack it at speed, with the skill of a mountain goat, or the elite runners will quickly leave you behind. This is the one skill (if that's the correct term to use) that separates mountain runners from their road or even cross-country counterparts. Every champion mountain runner has gained a bruise, lost some blood or even broken a bone or two from this 'skill' of theirs.

The zigzags below the monolith, marking the intersection of the Pyg and Llanberis Paths, allow onlookers to be astonished by the abilities of the runners. Wearing only running vests and shorts, the runners look out of place when compared with the walkers, in their outdoor clothes and carrying rucksacks. By now, the runners are more wet through due to the summit mist that's been engulfing them than the sweat they've produced on the lower sections of the route.

A quick turn at the top of Snowdon, and competitors can convince themselves that the hardest part is actually over. Statistically, though, the descent claims far more runners than the ascent. The Allt Moses section is notorious for bringing a runner's race to an early and abrupt halt. When walking this section of the Llanberis Path, the track seems reasonable underfoot; but if you try running down, as I had with Eve, Martin and Peter in July with the train as our pacemaker, all your thoughts are concentrated on preventing a fall. To run at the pace that Eve and the others were during the Eryri 32, meant that you had to have no fears at all about falling; you were running wild with little regard for safety. For those competitors at the front, taking any care is never about personal safety, it's about being able to finish the race first.

Eve had established herself as the first-placed female as she passed the Llanberis Path Halfway Café. There were just four men ahead of her, and the second-placed female, Liz Snedden from Scotland, was two hundred metres behind her. Depending on your overall position here, the final plan of your race will start to be put into action. Between Marco Rossi, the Italian in first place, and Liz were ten other runners including Eve. All of them were now formulating their final plan: win the race. Within the next minute, though, only eight of the ten were still in the running. John Fitzgerald from Ireland, who'd been in third place, had slipped on the final off-road section. Eve, who was hard on his heels, had instantly reacted and literally jumped over him. Unfortunately, a young runner from England hadn't reacted as quickly as Eve, and he now lay on the ground alongside John. Each would, hopefully, recover and finish the race. But their hopes of finishing in the top three would have to wait for another year.

As the race moved onto the first downhill stretch of tarmac, Eve was now in third place. The sight of the Mountain Rescue Land Rover was a green light for all of the runners to turn sharp right and run at full pace – not that they hadn't been doing that for the last twenty minutes of the descent!

When considering running a marathon, you will probably know the phrase 'hitting the wall'. In simple terms, this is when your mind and body have a disagreement. Your mind says, 'Keep going!' but your body says, 'Stop!' It's caused by a sudden loss of glycogen in your muscles. It's possible to run through 'the wall' and finish your race at a running pace if you're determined. But, ever since my first run with Eve, I'd realised that she didn't seem to acknowledge the existence of 'the wall'.

If they hadn't known better, the spectators along this section would have been forgiven for thinking that they were watching a one hundred metre sprint instead of the end of a thirty-two kilometre race. Only the final cattle grid, before Victoria Terrace, had any effect on their speed. But try as she might, Eve wasn't making up any ground on the first two runners. Worse still, Liz and her immediate followers were now narrowing the gap on her.

No matter how much you plan ahead, each race plan will be determined on the day the race takes place. This year, the sprint finish occurred far too early! It was supposed to happen during the last one hundred metres or so, on the flat tarmac of Llanberis' high street, not when there were one thousand metres to go, from the start of Victoria Terrace to the finishing banner. As Marco, Kevin Gilbert from England and Eve turned onto the main road through Llanberis, the three of them were still sprinting. There was no slapping of hands with the spectators lining the road as the trio hurtled past them. This year, first, second and third places were going to be decided on the finishing line.

With nothing 'left in their tanks' the sprint, amazingly, went on. Enid, standing next to me, looked like she was going to pass out and I could barely breathe myself! If any of them were hitting a wall, then it should have been Chinese in proportions, yet their competitive nature kept them going somehow. With two hundred metres to go, Eve passed Kevin. It wasn't that Eve had sped up (that would have been impossible); Kevin just couldn't keep his sprint going any longer.

At the final one hundred metres marker, both Eve and Marco could see the finish banner strung across the high street, with the official race clock showing the race time. The bright red digital numbers of the clock stood out, even in the midday sun, like a beacon beckoning them on. Large feather banners swayed in the gentle wind, advertising their clients, on the final section. Not that Eve or Marco would be reading any of these as they flew past.

Then it was fifty metres. Then it was twenty-five metres, and the two of them were running stride for stride. Suddenly, Marco raised both of his arms in unison, level with his chest, celebrating his second place as he finally surrendered to Eve and the pace she'd kept up since the start of Victoria Terrace. Amazingly, my advice had worked: 'two hundred metres from the end, get into second place, and one hundred metres from the finish line, overtake the person in front of you and stay in front.'

As she broke the tape, Eve pushed the stop on her yellow watch, which showed 1.59.23. I could see the official race clock, by the time I got to her, showing 2.00.14. When the results were given, Eve's sub two-hour time was found to be correct. As all the competitors wore a GPS-tracking device, there was no doubting her time. Not only had she come first, but she'd completed the thirty-two kilometres, with a height gain of over one thousand three hundred and seventy metres, in one hour, fifty-nine minutes and forty-six seconds.

Enid was crying and I, for once, was speechless. As Martin and Joe, laughing and cheering, gave Eve a celebratory lift up into the air, Liz Snedden interrupted them, hugging Eve and congratulating her, before her own support team had time to reach her.

'You know, it's cos you've got the best support team that you won,' Joe said, with his usual sense of humour.

Enid, now more thrilled than overwhelmed, was jumping for joy at Eve's success. She whispered to me, 'I can't wait till they ask us how we got on, when we get back to Pen-y-Bryn.'

At first, Eve's reaction was understated. Never one to let her emotions get the better of her, with 'deadpan' being her default expression, it's usually difficult to gauge how she's feeling. But as we walked back towards the minibus, Enid suddenly elbowed me in the ribs – obviously forgetting just how much it hurts when a Black Belt in karate elbows you.

As I cringed in reaction to her potentially deadly strike, she whispered with a smile on her face, 'Look at Eve.'

Usually never in last position when we were walking or running, now Eve was ambling along behind us and not really looking where she was going. With her winner's medal in one hand and the trophy in the other, she was simply gazing from one to the other. She was beaming, her whole face full of joy.

'Never seen that before,' Enid said and smiled.

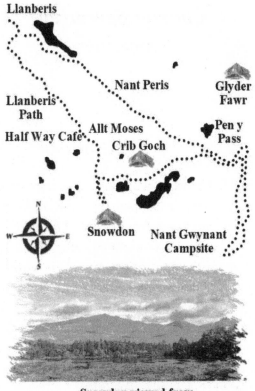

Llanberis

Nant Peris

Glyder Fawr

Llanberis Path

Half Way Cafe

Allt Moses

Crib Goch

Pen y Pass

N
W — E
S

Snowdon

Nant Gwynant Campsite

Snowdon viewed from
the Beddgelert Forest

*Route 12: The Eryri 32 – Thirty-two
kilometres long and approximately 1,400
Metres' height gain, including
the summit of Snowdon.*

Chapter Seventeen
Termination

November brought with it a surprising turn of events for me. Despite feeling happy and confident at both Ysgol Abaty and Pen-y-Bryn Hostel, I found it necessary to have my contract terminated, after discussion with Gareth Lee, at the start of the month. It would surprise many that it wasn't the challenging nature of the students or the unrealistic expectations of the parents and local authority representatives that caused me to do this. It wasn't even the endless paperwork – a considerable amount of which was unnecessary – that always had to be completed.

At the time, there was a national desire to be more inclusive, and for our students to experience mainstream settings. This is a controversial policy as there are many pros and cons involved, not only for the students, with their statements of educational needs, but also for the mainstream students attending these schools. The local authorities were deciding more and more to keep their students with special educational needs within mainstream schools. But the reality for me was that Ysgol Abaty, along with Pen-y-Bryn Hostel, was going to close, and at an accelerated pace. In fact, it was going to happen at the end of the autumn term. It was the considered opinion of the staff, after much debate, that this move was probably to reduce educational costs and wasn't for the benefit of the students at all.

Consequently, I was offered two positions at mainstream schools in Flintshire. These were as (a) a teacher of A Level English in a high school, a shortage area, and (b) as a Key Stage 2 primary school teacher. As varied a choice as you could possibly imagine! But after just over a year of working in an independent special school, I couldn't imagine teaching in a mainstream school again.

The two months that the students find most difficult at Ysgol Abaty and Pen-y-Bryn are the first one and the last one. Knowing this, I wasn't surprised when Dai Twice warned me of how difficult the last four weeks before Christmas were going to be. After all, there were nearly fifty students about to leave and I already knew, from my time at the school, that students find the transition process traumatic, not to mention the many management difficulties it was going to entail.

Since arriving at the school, I'd only witnessed two occasions when I realised why Joe was here rather than in an ordinary high school. The first time was when I helped to transport him to Pen-y-Bryn with Little Dave, after he'd fallen out with Alan. Thankfully, the brooding calm they'd both displayed hadn't led to a storm. He even joked about it later at dinner when he declared to Colin that he'd saved Alan's life. When Colin quizzed him about this some more, with a broad smile on his face, he'd explained:

'I stopped hitting him.'

Thankfully, Alan saw the funny side of Joe's joke and laughed out loud. 'Why aye, man, yous a reet canny lad.'

The second instance was at the end of the summer term when Priya had left. Joe had spent a lot of time supporting Priya with her training, so that she would pass the physical test for the army. Although they were no more than friends, I knew how hard it was for the students at Ysgol Abaty to allow friendships to come into their lives. They were always aware that one of them could move away at any time. Joe didn't display his feelings in a disruptive way. Priya had actually left in the penultimate week of the summer term for her basic-training course and for the last week of school, not even Eve could get Joe out of his room for any social interaction with any of the other students.

Now, the Christmas celebrations that staff and students always looked forward to were tinged with sadness due to the close-down. Even the tradition of wearing fancy dress wasn't thought appropriate. As local authorities had paid for the full term, this meant that parents wouldn't get any 'care allowance' until the start of the Christmas holidays if their children left earlier. The result of this was that probably all of the students would leave during, or at the end of, the last day of term.

*

It was both strange and sad to drive to Ysgol Abaty for that last school day in December, especially as leaving was not my own decision. The dinner ladies, as ever, put on a spread that would have pleased diners at any of the three-star Michelin restaurants that exist in the area – not that I've ever been to one of those, of course. It was the custom for staff members to wait on the students during the Christmas dinner – a sign of respect for the students. Even as the dinner ladies laughed and joked with the staff, as they picked up the plates of food from the serving hatch, you could hear the sadness in their voices.

Gareth Lee and Little Dave had agreed that all of the staff members should be present for the last day. This would obviously help with the practical needs of the closure but, in fairness, they'd made the decision on the grounds that everyone should be able to say goodbye or *hwyl fawr* to all of the students.

I was standing below the dining room's new double-glazed, UPVC window, taking in the scene. This was the first, and only, UPVC window to be installed in either the school or the hostel. The original wooden-framed one was beyond repair after Bethan's decision to put a chair through it. I wondered if the extra expense was really worthwhile in the circumstances, and concluded that it probably wasn't. Thinking back to the destruction that Bethan had caused in response to Colin dismissing her romantic advances, it seemed unbelievable now to see them sitting together, joking and laughing, as they enjoyed their Christmas pudding. Each was carefully dissecting their pudding, hoping to find a pound coin. This is the effect of inflation on the sixpence, or tanner, that I looked for in my Christmas pudding about fifty years ago! If Bethan and Colin ended up in the same home, I wondered if romance could follow – if so, I hoped they wouldn't become a modern-day 'Bonnie and Clyde'!

There was what I considered to be a senior boys' table, with Joe, Roy, Martin, Peter and Alan sitting at it. Joe and Roy had the other three lads crying with laughter as they recounted some of the adventures they'd shared here. Occasionally, I overheard a description of an event I'd been part of and I had to stop myself from going over and sharing their laughter. But, knowing them all so well now, I could see how each one couldn't prevent the sadness in their expression from showing briefly from time to time. I wondered how many of the tears of laughter I was observing actually concealed tears of sorrow or worry as well. I knew that this was probably going to be the last time they could share such moments, so the time should be theirs alone. I was sure they'd keep in touch, initially at least, via Facebook or another social media site, but their chances of seeing each other again, considering their personal situations and home locations, were slim to say the least.

Enid called me over to join her and Alice. They'd been taking the time to speak to every student individually and to give them a memento of the time they'd shared. With that task done, they were now standing in the opposite corner of the room to me. Walking over, I thought of the first time I'd seen Enid. Actually, it would be hard to forget! She was dressed as Wonder Woman and was bringing a tray of drinks back to the other superheroes assembled in a corner of The Market Cross in Holywell. I never imagined then just how strong the friendships of those superheroes would become, and in such a brief time too. Enid and Alice were already planning a staff reunion. Between them, they had everybody's contact details.

'What do you think about a get-together in the New Year?' Enid quizzed. A rhetorical question if ever there was one!

'That's a great idea; just let me know when and where,' was my immediate reply.

Some students, like Priya, Stephen and Sean (who I always think affectionately of as Yorkie), had already left in a far more natural and positive way. Priya had kept in touch with Enid and Eve, not only through Facebook and other social media, but also by good old-fashioned letter writing. Enid had shown me photographs of Priya sunning herself on a beach in Gibraltar, while we were enjoying our usual North Walian winter. I was so relieved that she was there, and not in one of the army's more hostile outposts.

I'd heard nothing from Stephen since the summer, but we received news of Yorkie at the start of December.

The woody odour of freshly logged trees, accompanied by the distant buzz of a chainsaw, will always bring back nostalgic thoughts of Sean or Yorkie as the students had christened him. He was polite and courteous to everyone, forever with a smile on his face, and got on with both staff and students alike. One of the best Sunday activities I experienced during my time at Pen-y-Bryn was when I took Yorkie, Chris, Colin and Michael to a local mountain bike centre between Ruthin and Wrexham, which was about half an hour's drive from the school. The five of us had a perfect day out. We tackled the Black Route and came away without too many cuts and bruises. The funniest moment was when Sean decided to try and overtake the four of us on a narrow section of the track. On the left-hand side there was a steep drop to the valley below. On the right, a natural gutter about a metre wide filled with water, before the hillside disappeared steeply above us. Sean waited for his opportunity and then steered to his right along the gutter line. Standing high on his pedals and going as fast as he could, he shouted, 'Beeb, beeb!' as he attempted to pass us.

Although thirteen at the time, at this particular moment he appeared to be a happy toddler – an experience he'd perhaps missed out on when he was young. He'd expected there to be about six inches of water, which would be sprayed onto us by his wheels as he sped past. Instead, he'd entered a three foot deep, slow, stagnant stream. He looked like a Mississippi paddle steamer slowly sinking as he pedalled away, before coming to a halt in waist-high water. How we laughed! I really felt that I'd spent the day with four friends.

Unfortunately, the news we received in December was heart breaking. Sean had taken his own life, an all-too-common occurrence for those who have attended a special school. Now every time I pass this section of the mountain bike route, I think of Sean's overtaking tactics, which always results in a smile and a tear.

Eve was noticeable by her absence, but as I sat down next to Enid and Alice, she entered the dining room and promptly came over and sat with us. She was full of excitement, having just left Little Dave in his office. It seemed that Eve had decided to follow a career as a carer and Little Dave had given her his full support. Needless to say, all three of us agreed with Little Dave's decision.

Taxis arrived and left on a regular basis after lunch, occasionally collecting two or three students, but most often only one. So, from 2:00pm until 4:30pm, the only word that seemed to be voiced by everyone was, 'Taxi!'

Then, as if in a moment, there was only one student left: Colin. Simon was keeping him occupied by checking all the rooms for forgotten items. Colin welcomed the opportunity to 'plunder', as he called it, unwanted belongings. He was now in possession of a pack of playing cards and a Nike baseball hat. Simon was confident that these would never be claimed by anyone else now.

5:40pm arrived and Colin had the honour of nearly all of the staff members waving him goodbye as he disappeared around the corner of Pen-y-Bryn's drive. Needless to say, the feeling of disappointment at the closure of the school was as strong among the students as it was among the staff. This clearly showed as each one made their way down the drive for the last time.

By 6:04pm, with tears in my eyes, I also had to leave.

One by one, each student came to mind as I drove home. Of course, the one who stood out the most was Eve. I'd had the pleasure of teaching her for just four terms, yet she'd made an impression larger than any other student I'd ever taught. It would be easy to remember Eve as 'the girl who always wins', as Priya had described her to me when we first sat down to dinner together.

The nature of the school, especially when combined with the hostel, and the need to form positive relationships, meant that I and the other staff members knew Eve, and the other students, in a far more complex way than is usual in mainstream schools. This was the difference between teaching at Ysgol Abaty and any of the other schools at which I'd taught. It was also true that I knew more about the students than just their academic ability. At Ysgol Abaty, I felt that I knew the person first and their academic ability second. To me, that seems to be the right way round.

Eve was proof that no matter the circumstance, you can be a credit to your family, your school and, of course, yourself. Shortly after I'd started teaching her, in partnership with one of the high schools she attended, Dai Twice had arranged for her to take some GCSE lessons, rather than just attending for the experience of doing so. Eve had a complicated history of education. She'd attended several mainstream and special schools; she'd even had periods without any education at all. Joining the GCSE courses at the start of their second year, she'd gained three passes, one at grade A and two at Grade B: English, History and Mathematics respectively.

When the results arrived in October, she'd made the national press, as she was the first student from Ysgol Abaty to gain GCSEs at a high school. Maintaining its partnership with Ysgol Abaty until the end, the high school had allowed Eve to retake her Mathematics exam in January, even though Ysgol Abaty would be closed by then. This resulted in Dai Twice, who was always a Maths teacher at heart, finally achieving the A grade GCSE in Mathematics that he'd always wished for by one of his Ysgol Abaty students. Knowing the natural and gifted athlete that Eve was, I'm sure she'd have easily achieved a GCSE pass in PE too, given the chance.

Now, with Pen-y-Bryn also closed, Eve still chose to remain in North Wales, an area that she'd grown to love. She went on to attend the local College of Further Education and continued with her academic success. She kept in touch with Enid, not only on Facebook but by letter and phone calls. By now, the relationship between her and Enid was one of close friends, rather than student and key worker.

Eve, Enid, Simon and I are still able to get together for mountain walks every now and again. We've even talked about running, rather than walking, the Welsh 3000s. I wonder whether Eve could challenge Angela Carson's record with the right support?

The last time Eve and I were out walking, she brought along her boyfriend Rob, who's training to be a paramedic. He showed off his new Skoda Superb; it seems that Skodas have now become cars you want rather than need. Looking at its leather seats and its range of electronic gadgets, it had very little in common with my Fabia, except the badge. Then again, the badge was also different; the laurel-leaf garland was missing. Personally, I thought the original logo looked better; I blame Jasper Carrott for the change in its image!

'How's everyone at home?' I asked Eve.

'They're all well,' Eve replied, 'but I don't see them now as I have my own life.'

This was an indication of the independence she'd achieved.

At college, as expected, she'd done superbly, having achieved her Level 1 NVQ in Tourism and Leisure. She'd then decided to get her Level 2, so as to have a higher paid and more managerial post when she started work. The thought of work in the 'care industry' had dissipated, due to its expected low financial rewards. The highlight of the day occurred when she showed off the photographs, on her iPad, of her recent trip to New Zealand. Eve seemed to have achieved so much in such a short time. It was hard to associate this confident and successful young lady with the schoolgirl who used to just run.

Eve still has her challenges when it comes to facing the world around her. She made us laugh out loud when she told us the story of her driving lessons. After a year with several instructors, as well as a lot of money spent, she was advised to stop learning altogether by her last instructor. She said his words were: 'Stop driving before you kill someone!'

This brought back memories of the Eve I'd first met,

who confessed far too much far too quickly – always trying to reach the end before she'd actually left the start. Eve was someone who did all the right things, but didn't always get all the things right!

Colin also has a special place in my memory and not just because of the dramatic way in which he introduced me to Ysgol Abaty. However, my fondness for him was tried after one of his mischievous escapades.

'You still like me, don't you, Tom?' he anxiously asked, as I was trying to explain the negative consequences of his shenanigans.

'It's never you I dislike,' I replied honestly. 'I like you, Colin; it's the things you do at times that I dislike.'

I find too many people confuse these two feelings. It would be easy to dislike Colin for some of his antics. But the Colin who took care of me on my first 'Simon's day out' or the Colin who, although not a natural athlete, persevered with his triple-jump practice, won my heart. Despite hindrances from his peer group, he still endeavoured to do the right thing – for example, on our visit to Coastal Wood Products when he supported me and Simon in trying to get the other students back on the minibus. I'd never forget the Colin who could stop you in your tracks when you heard him singing. How could anyone not like that Colin? I now consider it highly pertinent that Colin wasn't just the first Ysgol Abaty student I saw, but also the last one.

My short time at Ysgol Abaty and Pen-y-Bryn Hostel will always be a part of my DNA now. There were so many personal highs and lows, and among them, hilariously funny and truly sad times. I now find that I always sit with my back to a wall when in a public space, just in case a chair or similar item comes flying towards me!

It was during our get-together at the end of January that Alice confided something in me.

'I always knew you'd get on well at Ysgol Abaty; at times having you around was like having an extra student,' she said.

My expression was pure puzzlement, so she continued:

'You're engrossed by timekeeping, Tom, and full of statistics. As for all your stories that start with "Oh, and that reminds me..."' She paused to giggle. 'And you smell things that trigger all sorts of memories. But you never say "smell" because your mother never liked you "smelling" things when you were young, so it's always "odour", "scent" or "perfume".' She chuckled once again. 'You really are on the spectrum, aren't you, Tom?'

My silence, for once, wasn't caused by a past memory or an 'odour', but a realisation of the truth in Alice's words. It seemed it was only my date of birth that had determined whether my time at Ysgol Abaty should be as a member of staff or a student. However, Enid was the one who was responsible for my laughter as I drove through Caerwys on my way home alone later on that night.

When at the bar and helping to carry the drinks she was paying for, much to her disapproval, I asked the young barman:

'Have you got a calculator my friend can use?'

Seeing the funny side, she laughed and said, 'I'll tell you the worst calamity I've had when rushing in the morning before putting my lenses in. I only went and used hair removal cream instead of toothpaste! Flavour's crap, but it's great if you've got a hairy tongue, I suppose!'

Now that my teaching days are behind me, whenever I'm out walking in the North Wales countryside and I see a flash of yellow in the distance, I wonder, even hope, that it might be Eve – someone I'm glad and proud to be able to call my friend.

Appendix

1.   Title: 'Delilah', Artist: Sir Tom Jones, Released: 1967, Studio: Decca & Parrot, Songwriters: Les Reed & Barry Mason, Producer: Peter Sullivan.

2.   Joss Naylor MBE was a fell runner from Wasdale Head in the Lake District, born in 1938. I first became aware of his exceptional ability when preparing to do the Welsh 3000s for the first time. Known as the 'Iron Man' I will let some of his records speak for themselves. As you read them and look at the dates, bear in mind his age:

1973: The Welsh 3000s – the fourteen peaks of Snowdonia in four hours and forty-six minutes.

1974: The Pennine Way: three days and four hours.

1983: The Lakes, Meres and Waters circuit of one hundred and five miles in nineteen hours and twenty minutes.

1986: (aged fifty) completed The Wainwrights in seven days.

1997: (aged sixty) ran sixty Lakeland fell tops in thirty-six hours.

2006: (aged seventy) ran seventy Lakeland fell tops, covering *more than fifty miles and ascending more than twenty-five thousand feet, in under twenty-one hours.*

3.   Title: Leisure, Author: Welsh poet William Davies (1871 - 1940).

4.   ADHD: stands for 'Attention Deficit Hyperactivity Disorder'. Characteristics include: poor concentration, being easily distracted, hyperactivity and impulsiveness. The student will appear to be behaving like a far younger child than their actual age.

Epilepsy: An excessive electric charge to the brain, often with little warning. This causes a seizure, affecting the body in a number of ways depending on the severity of the charge and where in the brain it is happening. This occurs at any time and lasts from a few seconds to minutes, with varying signs and symptoms. Many adults can manage their condition so that few around them will be aware of it.

Dyslexia: Originally a Greek word which describes the condition of having a difficulty with spelling, words or language. It does puzzle me as to why it was decided to use the word 'dyslexia' to describe this condition, when you consider it is a condition that makes it difficult for the person concerned to read or spell!

5.   Mountain Marathons such as the UMM are usually two day event. Teams of two compete over mountain routes, finding their way from one control point to another in the quickest time. They have to carry their own equipment and have a wild camp usually in a remote location during the two days. There are several classes that you can choose from, with the Elite Classes covering about seventy kilometers and four thousand metres of ascent. Always held in remote areas, the exact location is usually kept secret until forty-eight hours before the start.

6. Elizabeth Cadwaladr (1789 - 1860), known as Betsi, was born in Bala in 1789. The daughter of a Methodist minister, and one of sixteen children, moved to Liverpool to work as a maid at the age of sixteen. After travelling the world as a maid, she changed her surname to Davis in memory of her father Dafydd, as Cadwaladr was difficult for English people to pronounce. In France at the time of the Battle of Waterloo, she made the decision to help British soldiers suffering in the Crimean War. While working at a hospital run by Florence Nightingale, she quickly became frustrated by restrictions that were imposed on her. After disagreements with Florence Nightingale, she moved on to work nearer the action in Balaclava, tackling poor medical conditions and cutting through unnecessary bureaucracy. When she returned home in 1855, she was herself suffering from cholera and dysentery. She died a pauper in 1860 and is buried in Abney Park Cemetery, London.

7. Bara brith would translate into English as 'speckled bread'. It is a fruit loaf made with tea, and tastes delicious with salted Welsh butter. Though there are many individual 'family' recipes, here is a common one:

Ingredients: 450g/1lb dried mixed fruit, 250g/9oz brown sugar, 300ml/½ pint warm black tea, 2 tsp mixed spice, 450g/1lb self-raising flour, 1 free-range egg beaten.

Method: Put fruit and tea in a large bowl, cover and leave overnight. Add the rest of the ingredients to this bowl and mix thoroughly. Preheat the oven to 170°C/325°F/Gas mark 3. Prepare a 900g/2lb-loaf tin with greaseproof paper. Add the mixture to the loaf tin and leave in the oven for 1½ hours.

8. Title: 'Baby, it's Cold Outside', Artists: Sir Tom Jones

& Cerys Matthews, Released: 1999, Label: GUT/V2, Songwriters: Frank Loesser 1944.

9. Title: *Mountaincraft and Leadership*, Author: Eric Langmuir, Published: 1969, Publisher: The Scottish Sports Council, The Mountain Leader Training Board.

10. Title: *I Bought a Mountain*, Author: Thomas Firbank, Published: 1940, Publisher: Four Square.

11. Colin Donnelly managed to break the legendary Josh Naylor's Welsh 3000s time by a remarkable twenty-seven minutes. He has held the records for the Buckden Pike Race and the Shelf Moor Race, having set them over thirty years ago. In 2019, a modern-day legend came along: Finlay Wild who, like Colin Donnelly, is Scottish and winning races and breaking records all over. In 2019 he set the new record of four hours, ten minutes and forty-eight seconds for the Welsh 3000s.

12. Angela Brand-Barker nee Carson has held her Welsh 3000s record for over thirty years. As well as winning the British Fell Running Championship many times, she also was the British Long-Distance Mountain Bike Champion in 2015.

13. Title: 'Walking on Broken Glass', Artist: Annie Lennox, Released:1992, Label: BMG & Arista, Songwriter: Annie Lennox, Producer: Stephen Lipson.

14. Title: 'Perfect Day', Artist: Lou Reed, Released: 1972, Label: RCA, Songwriter: Lou Reed, Producers: David Bowie & Mick Ronson.

15. Robin Bone was born in Canada in 1994. Originally, she trained as a gymnast but changed to pole-vaulting after suffering five concussions by the age of sixteen. Initially, she was teased at events for wearing a helmet, a proviso without which she would not have been able to compete. Bullies would laugh

and call her 'helmet girl'. This only motivated her to achieve greater heights, gaining state and Canadian Championship victories. Easily distinguishable when competing, as she always wears a protective helmet when jumping, she went on to achieve a personal best of 4.36 metres and represented Canada at the 2016 Rio Olympics.

16. Title: 'Cartwheels', Artist: Ward Thomas, Released: 2016, Label: Sony Music, WTW Music, Songwriters: Lizzie Ward Thomas, Catherine Ward Thomas, Rebekah Powell, Jessica Sharman, Glen Scott, Producers: Martin Terefe, Jimmy Hogarth.

Ward Thomas is the surname of twin sisters Catherine and Lizzy, born in 1994 in Hampshire. Their first Album From Where We Stand reached number one in the British Album Charts. This is surprising, not because it was their debut album, but because it was Country Music. By combining the sound of American country music with British lyrics, they have seemed to find an internationally successful formula.

17. Finlay Wild entered his first fell race in 2005. Since then, he has won many races and broken several records. A legend who is still competing and does not confine himself to running, he was the British Ski maintaining champion in 2016.